THE GIVING HEART

The Giving Heart

Folktales
for Exploring Generosity

Stories selected and introduced by

MARGO MCLOUGHLIN

created in partnership with the Fetzer Institute

Salsbury House Press,
Victoria, BC

Ordering Information:
Please contact Margo McLoughlin at margostoryteller@gmail.com.

Library and Archives Canada Cataloguing in Publication

The giving heart : folktales for exploring generosity / edited by Margo McLouglin.
Includes bibliographical references.

ISBN 978-0-9916880-1-2

1.   Generosity. 2. Tales. I. McLoughlin, Margo, 1960–.

BJ1533G4.M35 2012   177´.7   C2012-906235-9

Edited by Margo McLoughlin with Megan Scribner, Wayne Muller, and Patricia Moore Harbour.

Cover design by revealcreative.ca
Illustrations by Jennah Vhay Fox.
Layout and interior design by Vancouver Desktop Publishing Centre.
Printed in Canada by Island Blue Printorium Bookworks on 100% recycled stock.

to Mark

Table of Contents

Part I: The Story Circle in Practice

Part II: World Tales of Generosity

Acknowledgments

The Giving Heart Story Circle comes out of ten years of exploration and application. Certainly story circles are not new. For millennia human beings have gathered in circles to spin a narrative of their experience and to reflect through myth and metaphor on the mystery of life. In many parts of the world, they still do. Since the advent of writing and the printing press, however, and even more so now that we have developed ways of telling stories in moving pictures, we have lost touch with our oral storytelling beginnings. We have mislaid the simple magic of human connection that is born when people gather to listen to a storyteller and to draw a story out of each other. The Giving Heart Story Circle comes out of just such a circle—a group of colleagues listening to a folk tale and then responding, each from his or her own perspective.

Mark Nepo, former program officer at the Fetzer Institute, planted the first seed when he initiated a cross-cultural exploration of generosity and assembled the Generosity of Spirit project team (Patricia Moore Harbour, Wayne Muller, Megan Scribner, Ian Simmons, and myself). Recognizing the potential of storytelling to generate valuable discussion and promote a genuine renewal of relationships, Mark organized several retreats to pilot Generosity of Spirit story circles. These included pilot retreats with the faculty of the University of Indiana medical school; the faculty at the California Institute of Integral Studies; K—12 teachers in Michigan; philanthropists at the Council of Michigan Foundations' annual conference in Traverse City; congressional staffers; and social justice activists in Mississippi.

Through the Fetzer Institute many valuable connections were formed to support the application and dissemination of the material. Rita Higgins and Kathy Agard at the Council of Michigan Foundations partnered with us to have many of the generosity of spirit stories appear on the Council's website.[1] Bonnie Allen, at that time president of the Center for Law and Renewal at the Fetzer Institute, suggested the Generosity of Spirit team contact Martha Bergmark of the Mississippi

---

1   The Learning to Give website offers lesson plans, activities, and resources to educate youth about the power of philanthropy (sharing time, talent and treasure). It is visited and used by approximately 130,000 teachers across North America every month. See www.learningtogive.org/materials/folktales for 75 generosity stories organized by character trait, wisdom tradition, geography and title.

Center for Justice in Jackson, Mississippi. As a result several Spirit of Justice retreats were held at the Gray Center near Canton, MS. Martha invited a number of social justice activists from across the state, including Susan Glisson of the William Winter Institute for Racial Reconciliation in Oxford, Mississippi and Leroy Clemons of the Philadelphia Coalition in Philadelphia, MS. A new collaboration followed these retreats: The Fetzer Institute and the Winter Institute, with support from the Kellogg Foundation, joined forces to design and implement the Welcome Table: A Year of Dialogue on Race, a series of retreats aimed at building relationships in diverse communities. Stories, storytelling, and poetry all played a part at these retreats. Estrus Tucker, Sally Hare, and Debbie Stanley brought their valuable knowledge of Parker Palmer's Circle of Trust model to the Welcome Table. Their creativity and collaborative spirit are much appreciated. Several staff members and consultants from the Winter Institute also brought their wisdom and insight. These included Dave Molina, Leroy Clemons, Charles Tucker, Jacquelyn Byrd Martin, and Patrick Weems. Many community members attended the Welcome Table retreats. Their honesty, humor, and willingness to explore new ways of relating through story are what made these story circles such a rich opportunity to learn how stories work on the ground.

Another site of exploration has been the Comox Valley, a small community on Vancouver Island where I lived for many years. Using the material from the Generosity of Spirit retreats, I offered several Liberating the Gift through Story workshops as well as a series entitled Awakening the Healer. I am indebted to my friend Marie Purcell who encouraged and supported me to design and implement these workshops.

Finally, many thanks to my colleagues Wayne Muller, for his humor and deep love of the mystery of being human, to Megan Scribner, for her clear focus on the practical application of our conversations, to Ian Simmons for his energy for change and his insight into human nature, to Pat Harbour for her generous wisdom and loving presence, and to Peggy Quinn for her practical support and attention to detail. This work was initiated at the Fetzer Institute and supported throughout by the Institute's vision of nurturing love and compassion in the emerging global community.

This manuscript was completed while I was Artist-in-Residence at the Centre for Studies in Religion and Society at the University of Victoria during the 2011–2012 academic year. I extend my gratitude to the director, Paul Bramadat and to all the staff—Leslie Kenny, Rina Langford-Kimmett and June Thomson. I would also like to thank Professor Yvonne Hsieh for her generous gift to the Centre, which allowed the creation of the Chih-Chuang and Yien-Ying Hsieh Award for Art and Spirituality.

Preface

Everybody is a story. When I was a child, people sat around kitchen tables and told their stories. We don't do that so much anymore. Sitting around the table telling stories is not just a way of passing time. It is the way the wisdom gets passed along. The stuff that helps us to live a life worth remembering.

—RACHEL NAOMI REMEN

Growing up in the 60s and 70s, in the golden age of television, my own life with stories mostly revolved around shows like Gilligan's Island, Bewitched and The Beverly Hillbillies. With the help of a few props, my friends and I re-enacted scenes in the backyard. For my brother it was Hogan's Heroes and later, Star Trek. We both read voraciously, wonderful books like the Narnia series by C. S. Lewis, and other adventure series by Enid Blyton and Arthur Ransome. Though I didn't know what oral storytelling was, I was blessed to have a teacher in Grade Three who spun elaborate tales about adventures with her older brothers in the woods of post-war France. I trace my early ambition to being a spy to hearing my teacher's stories.

I happened upon storytelling in the community setting one summer in the 1980s while visiting a friend in Toronto. Every Friday night local storytellers and story-listeners gathered in the hall at St. George's Church to share and hear stories. My friend invited me to come with him to this weekly event, the "Thousand and One Nights of Storytelling."[2] The structure was informal. Once a teller had finished, another would come forward from the audience, take the talking stick in hand, and perch on the wooden stool at the front of the room to tell a story. There was no

---

2   Since 1978, storytellers and story listeners have been gathering in downtown Toronto for an evening of oral storytelling. Visit www.1001fridays.org for more information.

distinction between professionals and non-professionals, though some were clearly developing their craft in that space. Others, like my friend Adrian, simply had a story they wanted to share. I was struck by the intimacy of the event, as well as the authenticity of the tellers.

A few years later, drawing on my background in theatre and my love of children's literature and folklore, I began telling stories myself. I fell in love with the art of storytelling. As a listener, I had experienced the magic of being transported by the artistry of a skilled storyteller. As a teller, I soon recognized the power of being the one holding the reins of the unfolding narrative. I realized I had an ethical obligation to choose my stories well, to consider who is listening and how the story might affect them. Storytelling opens a receptive space in the minds and hearts of listeners—this is why storytelling can be so powerful. This is why it matters what kinds of stories we tell.

As I started on the path of storytelling I was primarily interested in the performance aspect of the art. I listened to different tellers and set out to find my own style. I studied voice and discovered the skill of image-making.[3] At the same time, I began teaching elementary school, the ideal site to develop my skill as a storyteller.

In my first year of teaching my school held an event for families. I was asked to tell a few stories for the children and their parents. One story I chose was "Great Joy," a Buddhist tale about respect and the power of speech to cause harm or bring about good.[4] I remember a parent speaking to me afterwards and telling me how the story had touched him. It reminded him, he said, of a difficult situation at work. In fact, in listening to the story, he now saw what course of action he needed to take. This was the first time I experienced how a story can work as a metaphor in very practical, applicable ways. The deeper meaning of a story and its potential as a metaphor will be unique to each listener. In literal and figurative ways, each listener will receive the story from a different vantage point. Perception is shaped by many factors, including language, culture, education and life experience. Therefore, when we "see" the story as it is being told—without props or pictures—we are supplying our own images. Terms as commonplace as "road" or "forest" will conjure vastly different images, depending on where one grew up. It is no wonder we make connections between the stories we hear and our own lives. We've already been actively engaged in weaving a correspondence as we listen.

---

3   See Doug Lipman, *Improving Your Storytelling: Beyond the Basics for All Who Tell Stories in Work or Play.* (Little Rock: August House, 1999).

4   "Great Joy" is storyteller Rafe Martin's retelling of a Buddhist tale. It can be found in *The Hungry Tigress: Buddhist Legends and Jataka Tales* (Berkeley, California; Parallax Press, 1990).

After telling stories that evening, I made a note to remember this incident, variations of which happened again and again almost every time I told stories. Someone would approach me at the end of the evening and say, "That story really helped me understand my father," or "Your story reminded me of the possibility of forgiveness."

And yet, even with all this evidence that my stories were calling to the stories of others, I still thought of storytelling as a one-way process. I viewed the storytelling event as performance, in which one person was the principal storyteller while the listeners received the gift of the stories and the storyteller's expertise. I had fallen into the trap of believing in the expert at the front of the room.

Luckily, life took me in new directions, ones that allowed my appreciation and understanding of storytelling to grow. I went to graduate school and became a chaplain, working part-time at Dana-Farber Cancer Institute in Boston. At the same time, I was hired to collect world tales of generosity for the Fetzer Institute's Generosity of Spirit Project. The initial aim of the project was to create a database and anthology of world folklore on this theme. My colleagues included poet and philosopher, Mark Nepo, at that time a program officer at Fetzer; author and teacher, Wayne Muller; writer and editor, Megan Scribner; activist and social entrepreneur, Ian Simmons; and later Pat Harbour, founder of Healing the Heart of Diversity®, a nonprofit organization dedicated to providing diversity leadership education.[5]

We fell into the habit of opening our meetings by listening to a story from our growing collection of folktales. We noticed that telling or reading the story out loud—not reading it silently and separately—created a special kind of space where we could better hear and learn from each other. After a while, we realized that we had stumbled upon one of the real gifts of storytelling—the opening of a space for reflection and shared stories.

We also discovered that the wisdom traditions of the world have a story for every aspect of generosity of spirit, from pride in generosity to fear of giving, from the expectations that generosity creates, to the delight and surprise of receiving just what is needed. We learned that when a story is told or shared in a circle of listeners who are given time and space to respond, the story's meaning is extended and amplified as the listeners hear each other's ideas and reflections. Alternative perspectives come into view and unexpected insights startle one out of one's habitual way of seeing. New relationships are formed through the shared experience of the story.

---

5   Over the years, many others contributed to the project, including Peggy Quinn, Jomie George, Zelene Wilkins, and Deborah Higgins.

I began to apply what I was learning about story to my work as a chaplain at Dana-Farber. I prepared a storytelling series for patients, family, and staff. On Wednesdays, over the course of several weeks, I set up the chapel with the heavy wooden chairs arranged in a circle. When a number of listeners had trickled in and found a seat, I welcomed them and told a story. Then, after a few moments of silence, I invited them to share their thoughts.

One day I told a Scottish folktale called "The Lady's Loaf-Field." In this story, a miserly lord reluctantly agrees to his wife's request that he give the wheat from one of his fields to make loaves of bread for the poor. His one condition is that she herself has to walk around the field. Though she is ill, the lady manages to do this with the help of two strapping young lasses, one on either side.

After I had finished telling the story, a woman who was undergoing treatment for cancer remarked on the role of the young lasses. This was the image that had stayed with her, reminding her of how grateful she was to have dear friends at her side. Listening to this first comment, another patient remarked that she was so used to being the one her family and friends relied on that it was difficult for her to do any "leaning." In listening to the story, she recognized how much she disliked being the one in the position of receiving help. The other listener's comment had suggested to her another way of viewing her situation. For a staff member, a researcher, who was present, the key element in the story was the idea of legacy. What difference would her work make to others? By sharing our reflections in the safe space of the story circle, very different participants in the life of the institution learned about each other's experience.

Understanding how fruitful storytelling is for inviting people into dialogue and relationship with each other, the Generosity of Spirit project piloted a series of retreats using our collection of world tales of generosity. Between 2005 and 2011, we created story circles in a number of different settings including health care, education, politics, philanthropy, and social justice. The aim in each setting was slightly different: to offer opportunities for vocational reflection and renewal; to inspire and educate; to build relationships and identify common values; to move beyond historical division and create healthy communities.[6] But whatever the goal, we found that using stories and carefully crafted questions created the space for the work that needed to be done.

Following these successes, we believe the time is right to make this material available to a wider audience. We have created this guide to help you begin your

---

6   To read about the Generosity of Spirit project's collaboration with the William Winter Institute for Racial Reconciliation, please see Appendix I, "Story Water/Story Wisdom," reprinted from *Parabola Magazine*, Summer, 2011.

own story circles. Here you will find many of the stories used in Generosity of Spirit retreats, as well as guidelines and suggestions for how to prepare and lead a Giving Heart Story Circle. This is a place where every voice is welcome, where the generosity stories of the world call to our own stories, inviting us to discover and express the gems of wisdom and insight that have been there all along.

Margo McLoughlin
Victoria, BC
August, 2012

PART I
_____

THE STORY CIRCLE IN PRACTICE

THE GIVING HEART STORY CIRCLE

Communities of care are sustained by rituals of regard.

—BELL HOOKS

We all have stories. But how often do we offer our stories as a gift? How often do we put down our work and patiently, even lovingly, receive the gift of another's story? Sharing stories is a ritual of regard. Wherever and however the storytelling begins, something transformational is soon underway: a quiet entering into another's memory and experience, a dissolving of barriers and limited ideas of who I am and who you are. In the listening and telling, there is a weaving of connection, an uncovering of the reciprocity of knowing that we call relationship. Storytelling reminds us that we are not alone, neither in our experience of grief and loss, nor in our concern for the world. When we share who we are through story we discover that our joys and sorrows are both unique and universal.

The story circle, consciously created, opens a space for listening with care. In this space, stories and story sharing bring into existence a community of care. We may ask, "What is meant by this idea of community?" Or "Which community is being referred to?" The answers will be different for each one of us. For some, the basic unit of belonging is one's family and friends, and therefore community refers to those who share a common history and a set of shared narratives. For others, community means geography—the neighborhood or landscape within a larger geographical area. Nowadays, community often refers to a group of people with shared interests—gender identification or sexual orientation, the pursuit of a certain spiritual practice or the commitment to a religious tradition. Leisure activities, cultural heritage, or political affiliation also create community. Asking, "Where do I experience a feeling of belonging?" is helpful in identifying a core community. However, there is a great need for each of us to build bridges of understanding by reaching out to those whom we see as different or "not my people." A story circle can be a place of intersection, where we weave connection through sharing and hearing each other's stories.

Planning a Story Circle

First Steps

Before finding a space or choosing and preparing the stories, it is helpful to stop and think about what motivates us to create a story circle. Knowing what honest intentions move us to share stories with a particular group at a particular time will allow us to recognize when something beneficial and useful has grown in the soil of our time together. In a culture that measures success in specific outcomes, it is important to create the space for stories that evoke deep human qualities that refuse to be so easily measured. Some things—trust, honesty, collaboration, love, shared community—are too precious, even magical, to be counted in the currency of the world. But there are other currencies, other forms of wealth, that can be liberated and invested if we take great care in preparing the soil in which we hope these stories will be shared.

If our aim, for example, is to build healthy relationships within a diverse group, then it might be helpful to consider what markers would indicate success. Increased trust, ease, mutual interest and concern—these might be indicators that the story circle can contribute to building healthy relationships. If the goal is to identify a common vision for the future, then the markers might be a mutually agreed-upon vision statement, or an agreement to work towards the creation of such a statement.

In some communities, people may have good reason to mistrust one another. There may be substantial hurt, misunderstanding, even violence that has lived and been passed through generations in the hearts of those in the circle, even those who genuinely seek to heal their community. A story circle, with a solid foundation, can become a safe place in which people can tell the truth, and feel seen and heard, with mercy, and without judgment. This alone can seed magnificent changes among people who have been secretly aching to work together, prevented only by their fear of endlessly experiencing the all-too-painful past.

When people who have little reason to trust one another—with long histories of enmity, hurt, and a lingering refusal to cooperate, have gathered in a story circle, we have seen transformational, structural and real racial and political healing where few expected it could happen.

Questions to ask:

Who will be present in the circle?
Some questions to think about: Who needs to be in the circle, as representatives of communities within the larger community? How do we make sure to include all the voices? How do we create an experience that is relevant and inspirational for them?

How do we prepare for this specific group?
Consider who will be attending this story circle. What are some important issues for them? For example, if it's the youth in a particular region, spend some time with representatives of this population and take note of the issues that are current for them.

Who will facilitate?
Also, who will facilitate the conversation? Will it be the same person every week, if it's an ongoing story circle, or a different member of the group for each gathering?

Where will we gather?
Is there a neutral space that would be inviting and accessible for people to attend? Is it possible to organize a meal to be shared before or after the story circle? Will there be a need for childcare or assistance with transportation? These are important questions. There are many factors that will support individuals in participating in a story circle.

What is our aim?
What are our common goals for the community? Have these been identified or is this a question that needs to be asked of those who join the circle? What stories appear to resonate with these goals?

Preparing the Structure and Content of the Story Circle

Structure
Think about how you want to structure the gathering. How long will it be? An afternoon or a morning? An entire day? Is it going to be a series of gatherings?

Introductions
What might be a good way of having people introduce themselves? In considering the issues of concern, is there a question that invites people to share a little bit about who they are without feeling too exposed? One question that we used at Welcome Table retreats in Louisville, Mississippi was "What do you love about the place you call home?"

Other ideas: "Where do you go to get recharged by nature? Is there a park, a beach, or a creek near you?" "Describe something that caught your attention recently as an example of people working together." "Tell the history of your name. Who gave it to you? Were you named for someone?"

Choosing the stories

What stories might work?

Review the stories. Find the ones that speak to you, or which you think relate in some way to the concerns of the group. Every folktale has its own themes, its own particular emphasis, its own language and rhythm. To choose a story for use in a story circle, here are some ideas: Take some time to get to know the stories in the collection. Read one at a time. When you've read a story, allow yourself to be with it. Notice the feelings, questions, or associations that surface. Does the story trigger any memories, or stories from your own life? Does the story feel complete to you, or is there something unresolved about it?

If you are working with a particular group you may be aware of goals or concerns that are current. What kind of story might be helpful in reinvigorating the group's vision or renewing mutual trust? A story about cooperation, or perhaps a story about leadership or dreaming?

Working with the stories

There are many different ways to lead a story circle. These range from leading discussions that are very open-ended to directing participants in more guided reflections. It's important to offer both kinds of experiences.

Examples:

1) After telling the story (or reading it aloud) allow the participant-listeners to sit with it for a minute in silence, then invite them to respond and reflect in the large group.

2) Or, invite participants to reflect in the large group for five to ten minutes and then have them break into smaller groups of five or six to share their reflections. After twenty minutes, participants come back to the large circle to share their thoughts.

3) Suggest a specific question for the participants to consider in the small group— one that relates directly to the story. (Examples follow most of the folktales in the collection.)

4) Groups of two. Allow some time for reflection in dyads so that everyone has a chance to speak since there are many people who will not speak in a large group, but who are comfortable sharing their reflections with one other person. This partner work needs to be carefully introduced, so that it doesn't become a casual conversation, but rather is a structured opportunity for each

person to speak, uninterrupted, for a short period of time, such as three or four minutes. One person speaks, while the other listens, offering their presence and support in non-verbal ways. Then, at the sound of a bell, the roles are switched. When both have had a chance to speak there is the possibility of asking clarifying questions and discussing the story and the experience of being listened to in this way. This work in small groups is a good opportunity to ask more challenging questions, such as, "What transformative gift have you received in your life?" (following such stories as "A Drum") or "Describe an experience of deep listening" (following "What Happens When You Really Listen.")

5) Triads. Similar to the work in pairs, but this time there are three people. One is the speaker, one the listener, and the third is the witness. The role of witness is an active role, holding the space, offering support to both the speaker and to the listener, simply by being present, eyes open or closed. When these groups of three return to the larger circle invite reflection on the experience of being a witness.

Tracking Your Story Circle Practice

Telling stories in a circle is an exploration in building relatedness by introducing new ways of holding a conversation.[7] How will you keep track of your learning? A blank journal, a spiral bound notebook, a three-ring binder, a Word Document on your laptop—any way of documenting a particular story circle's development and discoveries will help you refine and deepen your understanding of how these stories of generosity work.

Designing questions

When reading the stories, jot down three or four possible questions for each story. The questions could refer specifically to the story itself, or they could take the story as a starting point and invite participants to use it as a metaphor for their own experience.

Examples:

Specific questions for A Drum, page 62
Where is generosity present in this story? Who do the gifts in this story belong to? What do you think made the boy capable of giving in this way?

---

7   See Peter Block, *Community: The Structure of Belonging.* (San Francisco: Berrett-Koehler Publishers, Inc., 2008).

General questions

What gift have you received that you are now passing on? (Material objects or gifts in the sense of attitudes, perspectives, qualities of heart and mind.) Who are the models of generosity in your own life? How have you been surprised by generosity?

Specific questions for The Chief of the Well, page 66

Why do you think God appoints the lizard as caretaker of the well? Why do the animals listen to the lizard when he tells them the well is dry? What motivates the lizard, in your opinion?

General questions

What is the difference between a gatekeeper and a caretaker? What might the water represent in your own life?

Additional Exercises

What do you love?

Ask the group to form smaller groups of four or five. Give the instruction to state simply and clearly something (or someone) that you love. Each person at a time will speak one sentence into the circle. After a pause, the next person will then make their statement, which may or may not be influenced by the first person's words. The listeners are reminded not to comment or ask questions, but just to receive. Moving at a relaxed pace the sharing continues around the circle for several minutes, until a bell signals the end. Allow participants to sit quietly and feel the effects of this sharing, and then, when they have returned to the large group, ask them to reflect out loud on the experience.

Welcoming the Ancestors

If the story circle is taking place over an entire day or weekend, one beautiful exercise to include is the Ancestors' Circle. You may want to find a different space in which to lead this exercise, such as by a fireplace, or in a living-room with places for people to sit comfortably. Each of us has been inspired, nurtured, supported, encouraged, and loved by many people. In the Ancestor's Circle, we take turns telling a brief story of someone who has been a model, a mentor, or guide to us, saying his or her name out loud. As the speaker finishes, the facilitator repeats the ancestor's name, saying, for example, "We welcome Greg Morley into the circle."

Leading the Story Circle

Introduce the idea of the story circle. Think about why you are all sitting in a circle. It's about sharing wisdom! No one is the expert. Everyone has something valuable to say. When we sit in a circle everybody can see each other's face, as well as each other's body language. We are not hidden from each other. Instead we can be together and support each other in the circle.

Creating a safe space

The facilitator wants to support participants in feeling comfortable and safe with being in the circle. Prepare ahead of time by thinking about what the circle means. You might invite participants to share their own experiences of circles. What does gathering in a circle remind them of? What symbols are we enacting when we choose to arrange ourselves so that we can see each other in this way? The circle is important for many reasons, including the fact that in this configuration we see how we are mirrors for each other. We notice that another person's story is also one's own story. The circle is a symbol of continuity in the life cycle. It represents the truth that we are continuing the work begun by others, and we, in turn, will pass it on. The circle reminds us as well of our common humanity. It supports us to focus from within, develop a community of learners and deepen our understanding of each other.

Ways of beginning

Begin the event, as is done in indigenous cultures, by inviting everyone to declare their presence and readiness to participate by saying their name and where they are from.

Principles for creating a safe space

1) Provide a context that clearly allows participants to establish ownership of the experience individually and collectively.

2) Encourage presence. "I am here" is a declaration to be present and participate fully.

3) Request confidentiality. A guideline for participating must be that all participants are asked to maintain confidentiality Acknowledge that although the facilitator cannot guarantee confidentiality will be maintained for others, participants can individually commit and demonstrate in their actions that they will maintain confidentiality. To be responsible for personal confidentiality and hold an expectation for others contributes to and promotes a safe space. Moreover this expectation gives the responsibility, accountability, and ownership to the participants for maintaining confidentiality.

4) Encourage participants to take risks by stepping out of their shells, expanding their limited viewpoints, to try on new possibilities and be open to influence by others. Once one person takes a step that is outside their usual

pattern, another person will do the same. The circle begins to feel more connected and safe and the group begins to own the circle.

5) Deep listening to one another creates a safe space and increases the understanding between one another. This results in connectedness, community, and relationships beyond boundaries of difference.[8]

Introduce yourself. Perhaps share a story from your own life. Now you are ready to begin!

---

8   Many thanks to Pat Harbour for her contribution to this material on creating a safe space. For a more detailed list of group communication guidelines, see the Basic Circle Guidelines, as developed by Christina Baldwin in *The Circle Way: A Leader in Every Chair* (San Francisco: Berrett-Koehler Publishers Inc., 2010) available at www. peerspirit.com. Another set of guidelines for creating safe space is The Touchstones, as developed by Quaker educator, Parker Palmer for Circles of Trust.

PART II

WORLD TALES OF GENEROSITY

ONE

DREAMING

A dream you dream alone is only a dream. A dream you dream together is reality.

—JOHN LENNON

The notion of dreaming conjures a slowed-down receptive mode of being, open to random associations. We don't usually equate dreaming with action. And yet dreaming is where we begin to imagine a new world. Dr. Martin Luther King's famous speech "I Have a Dream," delivered on August 28, 1963 at the Lincoln Memorial in Washington, DC spoke vividly to the need for dreaming. Dr. King's words and the sound of his voice speaking them still echo into the twenty-first century. With each image that he spoke out loud he brought the reality of racial justice closer. On reading the text of Dr. King's speech one image in particular stands out for me:

> *I have a dream that one day even the state of Mississippi, a state sweltering with the heat of injustice, sweltering with the heat of oppression, will be transformed into an oasis of freedom and justice.*

I see the legacy of Dr. King's dreaming in the good work that is being done right now in Mississippi. At a Spirit of Justice retreat held near Jackson, Mississippi at the end of January 2006, I listened to twenty participants from the legal, civic, and education sectors share their vision for the state. Each of them had been invited to attend by Martha Bergmark of the Mississippi Center for Justice, an organization whose mission is to make Mississippi the social justice state. Over the course of two days, many important questions were raised, such as "How do we weave together these diverse groups in our community?" How do we open to another in a real way?" "In what ways can generosity lead to change in the system?" Stories from the Bible, from India, Ecuador, Haiti, and Kazakhstan helped to jump-start the conversation, offering vivid metaphors for the complex task of community building. Comments at the end of the retreat reflected the understanding that self-renewal is a crucial part of any form of service, since the work of giving is never done.

Dreaming is an essential step on the path to personal and social transformation. This is why we need artists, musicians, writers, dancers, and storytellers—to help us dream a new world. And new worlds are needed at the moment: worlds where every child is valued and loved, where clean water is a birthright, and care of the environment is the responsibility of everyone.

Stories of dreaming remind us of the role of the mind in giving birth to the world we live in. We dreamed it up and here it is. And because a story opens the door to imagination, it is a kind of active daydream. In the restful, receptive mode of story listening, our imaginations are richly nourished by the images of the story-world. The story invites shifts in perception and opens us to new ways of seeing. Paradoxically, the story's dream-like nature can make us more conscious of how we bring the world into being through our thoughts, words, and actions.

"The Secret of Dreaming," a retelling of an aboriginal Australian creation myth, describes the hard work of dreaming, how even when the dream becomes something real and tangible, it still needs to be cared for. The various creatures who receive the secret of dreaming recognize their own limits and pass the secret on to another, until the first humans receive it.

> And Man and Woman knew through the Dreaming,
> that all creatures
> were their spirit cousins
> . . . and that they must protect their Dreaming.

What is this secret of dreaming? Perhaps it is simply knowing that the dream must be cared for, that community building is the art of hearing each other's dreams and weaving the webs of connection that allow us to protect and care for them together.

The Secret of Dreaming

ABORIGINAL (AUSTRALIA)

For the Aboriginal people of Australia space and time are woven together. All living creatures and all features of the living landscape are interconnected. All are kin. Within this vast web of relationship everyone (and everything) has its place. Through ceremony and ritual the Aboriginal people activate the presence of their Spirit Ancestors, which is always with them. In this way they reconnect with the time of creation, known as the eternal "Dreamtime" or the "Dreaming." Through their ritual and stories they remember that humankind had a particular role to play in the Dreamtime, one that is not to be taken lightly, then or now.

Once there was nothing.
Nothing
but the Spirit of All Life

For a long time
there was nothing.

Then
in the mind of the Spirit of Life

. . . a Dreaming began.

In the empty darkness
there was a dreaming of Fire.

And the colour of Fire burned brightly
in the Mind of the Great Spirit

Then came a Dreaming of Wind,

and the fire danced and swirled
in the mind of the Spirit of Life

Then came a Dreaming of Rain

For a long time
the battle of Fire Wind and Rain
raged in the Dreaming

And the Great Spirit liked the Dream.

So the Dreaming continued.

Then, as the battle waned
between Fire Wind and Rain

There came a Dreaming
of Earth and Sky
and of Land and Sea.

For a long time
this Dreaming continued.

The Great Spirit began to grow tired
from the Dreaming,

but wanted the Dream to continue.

So life was sent into the Dream
to make it real,

and for Creator Spirits
to continue the Dreaming.

So the Spirit of Life
sent the Secret of Dreaming
into the world
with the Spirit of the Barramundi.

And Barramundi
entered the deep still waters,

. . . and began to Dream

Barramundi Dreamed
of waves and wet sand,

But Barramundi
did not understand the Dream
and wanted to Dream
only of the deep still water.

So Barramundi
passed the Secret of Dreaming
to the Spirit of the Currikee,
which is the Turtle.

And Currikee
came out of the waves
onto the wet sand

. . . and began to Dream.

Currikee Dreamed
of the rocks and warm sun.

But Currikee
did not understand the Dream,
and wanted to Dream
only of the waves
and wet sand.

So Currikee
passed the Secret of Dreaming
on to the Spirit of the Bogai,
which is the Lizard.

And Bogai
climbed onto a rock
and felt the warm sun on his back,

. . . and began to Dream.

Bogai Dreamed
of the wind and the open sky.

But Bogai
did not understand the Dream

and wanted to Dream
only of the rocks
and warm sun.

So Bogai
passed the Secret of Dreaming
onto the Spirit of the Bunjil,
which is the Eagle.

And Bunjil
rose into the open sky,
felt the wind in his wings,

. . . and began to Dream.

Bunjil Dreamed
of the trees and the night sky,

But Bunjil
did not understand the Dream
and wanted to dream
only of the wind
and open sky.

So Bunjil
passed the Secret of Dreaming
onto the Spirit of the Coonerang,
which is the possum.

And Coonerang
climbed high into the tree,
looked at the night sky,

. . . and began to Dream.

So Coonerang Dreamed
of wide plains and yellow grass.

But Coonerang
did not understand the Dream,
and wanted to Dream
only of the trees
and the night sky.

So Coonerang
passed the Secret of Dreaming
onto the Spirit of the Kangaroo.

And Kangaroo
stood tall,
looked across the plain of yellow grass

. . . and began to Dream.

Kangaroo Dreamed
of music, and song and laughter.

But Kangaroo
did not understand the Dream
and wanted to Dream
only of the wide plains
and yellow grass.

So Kangaroo
passed the Secret of Dreaming
onto the Spirit of Man and Woman.

And together they
walked across the land
and saw all the works of creation
They heard the birdsong at dawn
and saw the red sun at dusk,

. . . and began to Dream.
They Dreamed
of sharing the music of dawn birds,
the dance of the emu
and the red ochre of sunset

And they Dreamed also
of the laughter of children

And man and woman understood the Dream.

So they continued to Dream
of all the things
that had been dreamed before.

They dreamed
of the deep still water,
of the waves and wet sand,
the rocks and open sky,
the trees and the night sky,
and the plains of yellow grass.

And Man and Woman knew through the Dreaming,
that all creatures
were their spirit cousins

. . . and that they must protect their Dreaming.

And they Dreamed
of how they would tell these secrets
to their child
who was not yet born.

Then the Great Spirit knew at last

that the Secret of Dreaming was safe.

And being tired
from the Dreaming of Creation,
the Spirit of Life entered the land
to rest

So that now,
when the spirits of all creatures
become tired

they join the Spirit of Life in the Land
So this is why the Land is sacred

and we must be its Caretaker.

Barramundi (Barra-MUN-dee): A species of fish, native to the Indo-Pacific region.

Currikee (KOOR-ik-ee): A salt water turtle.

Bogai (BOG-eye): A large red throated lizard.

Bunjill (BUN-jill): A wedge-tailed eagle.

Coonerang (CUHN-er-ANG): A ring-tailed possum.

STORY CIRCLE PRACTICE

Consider asking different members of the circle to read the story aloud together.

REFLECTIVE QUESTIONS

ᔥ *Do you have permission to dream?*

ᔥ *If you did, what would that look like?*

STORYTELLING

ᔥ *Why is dreaming important? How are we keepers of each other's hopes and dreams?*

Tell a story about hearing someone else describe his or her dream. How did that feel?

Tell a story about having someone listen as you described your dream. How did the way you were listened to help you or not?

ᔥ *Whose dream are we caring for?*

Tell a story about a vision you have for your community.

The Magic Pillow

CHINA

Taoism and Confucianism were the main religions of Feudal China. In the 4th century BCE, the Taoist philosopher Yang Chu wrote: "What is man's life for? What pleasure is there in it? Is it for beauty and riches? Is it for sound and colour? But there comes a time when beauty and riches no longer answer the needs of the heart, and when a surfeit of sound and colour becomes a weariness to the eyes and a ringing in the ears."

Once a Taoist priest who had acquired the magic of the immortals was traveling on the road to Hantan.[9] He had stopped at an inn and was sitting and resting with his back against his bag when he was joined in pleasant conversation by a young man named Lu Sheng. The young man wore a plain, short coat and rode a black colt. He had stopped at the inn on his way to the fields. After a while he suddenly sighed and said, "It is because fate is against me that I have been such a failure in life!"

"Why do you say that?" asked the priest. "As far as I can see you suffer from nothing and appear to enjoy the best of health."

"This is mere existence," Lu Sheng said. "I do not call this life."

"What then do you call life?"

The young man answered, "A man ought to achieve great things and make a name for himself; he should be a general at the head of an expedition or a great minister at court. He should preside over sumptuous banquets and order the orchestra to play what he likes. He should cause his clan to prosper and his own family to grow rich—these things make what I call life. I have devoted myself to study and

---

9   "Immortal" is one English translation for the Chinese word Xian, referring to an enlightened person. See *Wandering on the Way: Early Taoist Tales and Parables of Chuang Tzu* by Victor H. Mair, (New York: Bantam Books, 1994).

have enriched myself with travel; I used to think that rank and title were mine for the picking, but now at the prime of life I still have to labor in the fields. What do you call this if not failure?"

As he finished speaking he felt a sudden drowsiness. The innkeeper was steaming some millet at the time. The priest reached into his bag and took out a pillow and gave it to Lu Sheng, saying, "Rest your head on this pillow; it will enable you to fulfill your wishes."

Lu Sheng laid his head on the pillow. He found himself back home. A few months later he married the daughter of a certain family, a young woman who was very beautiful and intelligent. His wealth increased by the day and he surrounded himself with luxury. The following year he joined the ranks at court. He was made a member of the imperial secretariat and had the honor of composing occasional poems at the Emperor's command. Many distinctions followed, including a series of provincial posts. He became the governor of Shensi, where he built a canal, which brought many benefits to the people of the region. He joined the Emperor's campaign against the encroaching barbarians, and succeeded in pushing them back. He conquered new territory and built three cities to defend the frontier. When he returned to court he was received with honor, but the other ministers grew jealous. Due to their slanderous attacks he was banished to a provincial post. Three years later, however, he was recalled to court, where he held the reins of government for ten years.

Then, once again, he fell victim to the jealousy of his colleagues. He was charged with conspiracy and thrown into prison. When the guards came to arrest him, he was stricken with terror and bewilderment. He said to his wife and sons: "Back in Shantung we have good land, quite sufficient to keep us from cold and hunger. Why should I have sought rank and title, which in the end have only brought calamity? It is now too late to wish that I could again ride back and forth on the Hantan road as I once did, wearing my plain hempen coat!" He drew his sword and was about to kill himself, but was prevented by his wife. Later, all those implicated in the plot were executed except Lu Sheng. He was exiled to Huanchou. But a few years later, the Emperor recalled him and made him president of the Imperial Council.

He had five sons, all of whom were gifted and were admitted into official ranks. They all married daughters of influential families and presented him with more than ten grandchildren. So he lived for more than fifty years, during which time he was twice banished to the frontiers and twice recalled to court where he was given even greater honors than before. He became addicted to pleasures and extravagance.

When advanced age made him wish to retire from court life, his petitions were refused. When he fell ill he was attended by the most eminent physicians. But all was in vain and one night he died, whereupon he woke with a start and found himself lying as before by the roadside inn, with the priest sitting beside him and the millet that his host was cooking still not yet done. Everything was as it had been before he dozed off.

"Could it be that I have been dreaming all this while?" he said, rising to his feet.

"Life as you would have it is but like that," said the priest.

For a long while the young man reflected in silence, then he said, "I now know at last the way of honor and disgrace and the meaning of poverty and fortune, the reciprocity of gain and loss and the mystery of life and death, and I owe all this knowledge to you. Since you have thus deigned to instruct me in the vanity of ambition, dare I refuse to profit thereby?'

With this he bowed profoundly to the priest and went away.

❦ ❦ ❦

STORY CIRCLE PRACTICE

REFLECTIVE QUESTIONS

§ *What ambitions drive our actions? Do we know why we are on a certain path?*

§ *What part of our lives is a dream and what part is real?*

§ *What good fortune is ours that we overlook?*

STORYTELLING

§ *What keeps you connected to your present life?*

Tell a story about something you do that keeps you grounded.

§ *What is your relationship to dreaming? Have dreams played an important role in your life?*

Tell a story about a dream that has been meaningful to you.

§ *Who are the wise elders in your community?*

Tell a story about an elder who enlarged your perspective in some way.

The Snake of Dreams

REPUBLIC OF GEORGIA

The small country of Georgia, located between the Black Sea and the Caspian Sea, includes territory that spans both Europe and Asia. Most parts of the highlands are situated on the northern and southern slopes of the Caucasus Mountains, the highest range in Europe. In Greek mythology the Caucasus, or Kaukasos, was one of the pillars supporting the world. After presenting man with the gift of fire, Prometheus (or Amirani in the Georgian version), was chained there, to have his liver eaten daily by an eagle as punishment for defying Zeus' wish of not giving the "secret of fire" to humans.

Many years ago—and it was neither my time nor your time—there lived a great king. And one night that king dreamed a strange dream. He dreamed that a fox was hanging by its tail from the ceiling above his golden throne, a red fox, snarling and snapping, suspended by its red brush. When the king woke up he called all of his advisers and wise men.

"What could be the meaning of such a dream?" But they all shook their heads and shrugged their shoulders and not one of them could find an answer to that question. So the king ordered every grown man and woman in his kingdom to gather before the palace.

"Surely," he thought to himself, "there must be someone in this great country who can unriddle my dream."

So the people came from north, south, east and west. And among the many there was one, a simple farmer who lived among the mountains far in the north. As he travelled towards the king's palace he came to a

narrow pass between two mighty mountains, and curled in the dust of the road there was a snake. As the farmer drew close the snake lifted its thin head:

"Aaaaaah, Traveller, stop, and tell me, where are you going?"

The farmer stopped in amazement.

"I . . . I . . . I'm going to the palace, the king has had a dream."

"And Traveller, do you know the meaning of this dream?"

"Me, I'm just a farmer. I know nothing about dreams."

"Well, Traveller, I can tell you its meaning, and if you tell the king he will reward you well."

"Then tell me, Snake, tell me now!"

"Aaaaaaah, Traveller, nothing comes from nothing. I will tell you only if you promise to share half of that reward with me."

"I promise, Snake, now tell me."

"The king has dreamed of a fox, hanging above his throne, and the dream means thisssssss."

The farmer crouched and the snake lifted its thin head and whispered into his ear.

The farmer listened, nodded and continued his journey, and after some days he joined the massing crowd before the king's palace. A trumpet sounded, the king's dream was told, and a great hush fell on the people. No-one could unriddle the dream.

But then, from the back of the crowd, came a voice:

"Majesty, majesty, your dream means this . . . "

"Bring the man forward!"

And the farmer was brought before the king.

"Majesty your dream means this: These are times of cunning and treachery, no-one is to be trusted, your kingdom is like a den of foxes."

The king nodded and smiled.

"The dream is well read."

From beneath his throne he took two bags of gold and gave them to the farmer. And the farmer set off for home, but he was careful to avoid the pass between the mountains, he went the longer way round and kept all the gold for himself.

And time passed.

Then one night the king dreamed a second dream.

He dreamed that a sword was hanging by a hair from the ceiling above his golden throne. A sharpened sword, flashing and spinning, suspended by a fine thread. And when he woke he called his messengers:

"Go and fetch that farmer from the north!"

When the farmer received the king's message his heart sank, but he knew there was only one thing for it, and he set off along the narrow pass between the two mountains.

"Snake, Snake!"

There was no answer.

"Snake, Snake, I need your help again!"

"Aaaaaah, Traveller, I am here."

"The king has had a second dream."

"I know, and I will tell you its meaning, but only if you truly promise to share half of your reward with me."

"This time, Snake, I truly promise."

"The king has dreamed of a sword, hanging above his throne, and the dream means thisssss . . . "

And the snake whispered into the farmer's ear.

The farmer continued his journey, and after some days he was standing before the king's throne.

"Majesty, your dream means this: These are times of anger and warfare, your enemies are preparing for battle, your kingdom is bristling with sharpened swords."

The king nodded and smiled.

"The dream is well read."

He gave the farmer four bags of gold, and he prepared himself for battle.

As for the farmer, this time he followed the narrow pass between the mountains, but when he saw the snake curled in the dust of the road waiting for him he was filled with anger and he drew his knife.

"Haaaaa, Traveller, you have brought me my share!"

"You'll have nothing but a black stone and a cinder!"

He chased the snake and hacked off its tail with his knife.

And he kept all the gold for himself.

And time passed.

Then one night the king dreamed a third dream.

He dreamed that the carcass of a sheep was hanging by its legs from the ceiling above his golden throne. A fat, dressed carcass, skinned and split like meat in a butcher's shop. When the king woke he sent his messengers to fetch the farmer again.

And the farmer knew there was only one thing for it. Swallowing his pride, he set out for the third time along the narrow pass between the mountains.

"Snake, Snake!"

There was no answer.

"Snake, please Snake, forgive me!"

There was no answer.

"Snake, I need you again."

"Haaaaa, Traveller, I am here."

"Snake, I beg you to forgive me, the king has dreamed again."

"I know, and I will tell you the meaning, if this time you swear to share your reward with me."

"I swear, half will be yours."

"The king has dreamed of a sheep's carcass, hanging above his throne, and the dream means thisssssssss . . . "

When the farmer had heard, he continued his journey until he stood before the king's throne.

"Majesty, your dream means this: These are times of ease and generosity, every belly in the land is full, your kingdom is like a fat carcass giving peace and plenty to all."

The king nodded and smiled.

"The dream is well read."

He gave the farmer six bags of gold, and the farmer made his way straight back to the pass between the mountains.

"Snake, Snake!"

The snake came and the farmer knelt beside it with tears in his eyes.

"Snake, now you must take all these six bags of gold, for truly it is half of all that I have won . . . and I have no words to tell you my shame at having treated you so badly."

But the snake lifted its thin head and shook it sadly from side to side.

"Traveller, Traveller, you have done no wrong, there is no blame. You are just one among many. When the kingdom was like a den of foxes, you too were treacherous and cunning and you went home the other way. When the kingdom was bristling with sharpened swords, you too were quick to anger and you cut off my tail. And now the kingdom is like a fat carcass giving peace and plenty to all, you too are suddenly filled with kindness and you offer me your gold. But, Traveller, what use have I, the oldest of the old and the wisest of the wise, for your paltry gold? Keep it and go in peace."

With that the snake slid into a crack in the rock and was gone.

And the farmer swung the bags over his shoulders and continued his journey— but suddenly the gold seemed heavy against his back.

❀ ❧ ❀

STORY CIRCLE PRACTICE

§ *How are we affected by our culture?*

§ *What kinds of promises do we make to ourselves or to others?*

STORYTELLING

Tell a story about a time when you saw clearly what the culture expects you to do or be.

Tell a story about a time when you swam "against the current" and made a different choice than the dominant culture might support.

The Revolt of the Utensils

TACANA—BOLIVIA

The Tacana Indians live in the rainforests of Bolivia. This tale is one of many stories that speak of the time of creation, when objects had the same interests as people.

In earlier times, wooden spoons, clay pots, and other household objects were like people. They spoke and visited each other back and forth. They danced and made *chicha*.[10]

One day the Master of a house went out. The utensils decided to go down to the garden and the stream to fetch maize and water to prepare *chicha*. They went down to the garden and the stream. They fetched the maize and water. Then they prepared maize *chicha*. They were delighted and said, "Now let us make music. Let us have some dancing." After they had prepared the *chicha*, they made music and danced. They were in very good spirits and conversed happily with each other. After they had celebrated for a long time they knew that the Master of the house would soon be returning. They began to tidy up and put everything back in its place. In a short time, everything was as before. The Master of the house came back. He looked around and said, "Everything seems to be in order." The utensils doubled over with laughter.

❋ ❋ ❋

---

10 Beer made from corn-maize.

STORY CIRCLE PRACTICE

ꝸ *How do you stay connected to a sense of mystery?*

ꝸ *What objects in your life seem to have a personality?*

Tell a story about an inanimate object in your life (Perhaps something you lost and then found in an odd place, or something that showed up just when you needed it.)

ꝸ *If a group of objects in your house were going to revolt, what would they get up to?*

Tell a story about the revolt of your candlesticks, doorknobs, pencil crayons . . .

TWO

GIVING AND RECEIVING

I realized this weekend that one can tell the tale and
leave the moral of the story to the reader.

—ANITA BATMAN

Greenwood, Mississippi, following a welcome
table retreat in Louiville, MS

Telling stories is all about giving and receiving. The storyteller offers the gift of her tale, but for each listener it will be a slightly different gift. As we respond to the images in the story we discover what it means to us. Likewise, when we hear how our fellow participants have received it, we learn something about who's sitting in the circle with us. We begin to recognize how alike we are, and how we can learn from each other. Together we give ourselves permission to settle back and listen to a story. The shared experience of listening begins to weave a feeling of connection and belonging.

A few years ago, many of the stories in this collection traveled with me to Mississippi where I told them as part of the Welcome Table retreats hosted by the William Winter Institute for Racial Reconciliation and the Fetzer Institute.

At one gathering I told the Indian folktale from Karnataka called "A Story and a Song," in which a housewife is unable (for unexplained reasons) to share her gifts—a story and a song. As a result the story and a song make their escape and the woman loses access to them. My friend and colleague Estrus Tucker led the group in reflecting on the story by asking us to consider three questions: "What are the gifts that are untapped in your community? What's suffocating those gifts, that capital? What would liberate them?" After a short reflection in the large circle we broke into smaller groups. In my small group, some of the ideas that emerged, in terms of untapped gifts, included gardening, music (specifically, community choirs), and the gift of listening. "What keeps this kind of capital and others like it under wraps?" we asked. The answers were clear: People believing themselves to be too busy; fear of criticism; complacency; resistance; lack of knowledge; and in many public schools, lack of texts, which results in children not having any experience with the discipline of doing homework. "What might liberate these gifts?" There was no shortage of ideas in response to this question. "Leadership," said one participant. "The system of leadership needs to be changed." "Imagination," said another. "Initiative. Being willing to challenge tradition." Other ideas included sharing experience, breaking bread together, the conscious creation of community, working from the ground up, and dialogue between generations.

Some questions that followed from this exploration included: What is the new language that is going to be needed? How do we revive relationships? How do we enter that conversation? Is what I'm doing today going to have an impact tomorrow, or five or ten years from now?

The work of building relationships is ongoing. A weekend workshop or retreat can be a model for new ways of relating. Sometimes, all that is needed is an opportunity to reframe the question. Instead of asking, "What's missing? What do we lack?" we can ask, "Where is the hidden capital in our community and how can we liberate those gifts?

At the close of the weekend my colleague Wayne Muller invited participants to consider the smallest thing they could do as a result of their experience at this retreat. Here are some of their answers:

"Tell people what happened."

"Talk with my friends about oppression."

"Expand the circle."

"Start a circle of pastors. Create relationships."

Stories remind us that this dance of reciprocity is what being human is all about—giving and receiving. It's never just one or the other. Always giving isn't sustainable or healthy. Always being on the receiving end diminishes our sense of initiative and energy. Creating community is about helping each other see generosity in a new light, not as something that one group has and one group must wait to receive. Rather it's about helping each other identify the hidden gifts we all have. Stories of generosity remind us to keep exploring and nurturing our capacity to give, even as we open more and more fully to receive the gifts that come our way.

Mokusen's Hand

A ZEN TALE (JAPAN)

The Zen tradition of Buddhism is filled with enigmatic teaching stories, often distilled to a single image. The essence of the transmission relies on an intuitive grasp of the teaching, rather than analysis.

A lay-disciple complained to Mokusen Hiki that his wife was too stingy.

One day, Mokusen visited the couple at their house. Mokusen showed a clenched fist to his disciple's wife. The surprised woman exclaimed, "What do you mean by that?"

"What would you say if my hand were always like that?"

"It's deformed."

Mokusen opened his hand wide and asked, "What would you say if my hand were always like that?"

"It's deformed."

"If you understand this, then you are a good wife."

After this visit, the wife helped her husband in spending as well as in saving money.

❈ ❦ ❈

STORY CIRCLE PRACTICE

REFLECTIVE QUESTIONS

§ *What images come to mind when you think of generosity or liberality?*

§ *What images come to mind when you think of stinginess?*

STORYTELLING

§ *How do you balance giving and receiving in your life?*

Tell a story.

Tiggak

INUIT

*This story was collected near Kulusuk, East Green-
land by Lawrence Millman. He writes: "Inuit folklore abounds in stories that show a connection between human beings and animals. That connection
is necessarily an intimate one, since without animals
the Inuit would have virtually nothing to eat. In
"Tiggak," this intimacy is carried to its logical end:
animals and humans share the same body parts."*

There was a man named Tiggak whose only son drowned in the sea. And
such a powerful grief came to the old man that he set up his hut right next
to his son's grave. The very first night he was awakened by noises. An ice-
bear, a walrus, a hare, and a fox were busy removing the stones from the grave.
Tiggak was furious and threatened them with his spear.

"But how do you think that we get our teeth?" said the fox.

"How do you think that we got our whiskers?" the walrus
said.

"And how do you think we got our genitals?" the hare said.

"We must perforce steal from the dead," declared the
ice-bear.

Whereupon Tiggak allowed them to take whatever they
wanted from his son. The grateful animals repaid his kindness many times over, for there wasn't a day after that when
he didn't have good hunting.

STORY CIRCLE PRACTICE

ဿ *What is hard for you to share? What is easy?*

ဿ *In what way do you experience the give and take of the universe?*

STORYTELLING

Tell a story about being asked to share something precious to you. *What happened?*

Tell a story about a time when you experienced the bounty and generosity of nature and the living world.

Mullah in the Turkish Bath

The stories of Mullah Nasruddin have been circulating throughout the world for the last seven hundred years. Was he a real person? Some scholars suggest that the Mullah (which means "teacher") was born in a Turkish village in 1208 and died around 1284. By turning our conventional ideas upside down, these Sufi tales awaken us to new ways of seeing.

Once Mullah went to a Turkish bath. The attendants ignored him. Upon leaving the bath, Mullah gave each of the servants two derhams as tip.

Next time the attendants gave Mullah special attention, hoping to get much more in tips than on the previous occasion.

Upon coming out of the bath, Mullah paid only one derham as a tip.

"Why is it that you paid us more in tips last time, but so little this time?" asked one of the servants.

"Well," said Mullah, "last time's tip was for today and today's tip is for last time," as the attendants looked at Mullah in astonishment.

❊ ❊ ❊

STORY CIRCLE PRACTICE

REFLECTIVE QUESTIONS

§ *How does it feel when generosity becomes an expectation?*

§ *What is it like to be rewarded when you don't feel deserving?*

STORYTELLING

Tell a story about finding a way to renew your feeling of generosity.

Tell a story about surprising someone with a gift, for the pure pleasure of it.

A Quick Crop

TURKEY

*This story comes from the writings of Sheik Mu-
zaffer Ozak. Born in 1916 near Istanbul, he was
educated by a succession of teachers who instructed
him in all branches of the Islamic tradition. He became Muezzin and eventually Imam to many of the
mosques of Istanbul. He later retired from the of-
fice of the Imam and preached the Friday prayers
at a mosque near the famous Istanbul book market,
where he owned a shop specializing in rare and an-
tique books. He was a prolific author in the Turkish
language. This story tells of Harun al-Rashid, an
eighth century ruler in the region which encompasses modern Iraq.*

Harun al-Rashid was once walking through a plantation when he saw a
hunched old graybeard putting in sapling date palms. He greeted him,
saying, "Take it easy, father!"

"Thank you, my son," the old man replied.

"What are you doing, father?" asked the caliph.

"As you see, I am planting sapling date palms."

"How many years does it take a date palm to bear fruit?"

"Ten, twenty, thirty years. Some take as long as a hundred years."

"Will you be able to eat the fruit of these palms you are planting?"

"I may not live to see the day," said the old man, "but we eat from those our
forebears planted. So let us plant, that those who follow us may eat in turn!" His
words impressed the caliph, who tossed him a purse of money. The old man took
the gold pieces, saying, "I give praise to Allah, for the saplings I planted have borne
fruit immediately!" The caliph was pleased to hear him say this, and he gave him
another purse of gold.

Said the old man, "I give praise to Allah, for trees normally bear fruit only once a year, but mine have produced two crops in one year!"

Throwing him yet another purse of gold, the caliph turned to the servant at his side and said, "Quick, let us get away from here before this old man leaves us penniless."

And off they went.

※ ※ ※

STORY CIRCLE PRACTICE

REFLECTIVE QUESTIONS

§ *What seeds are we planting as a gift to future generations?*

STORYTELLING

§ *In your family or community, what gifts have you received from your forebears?*

Tell a story.

Loosening the Stopper

HASIDIC

Founded in the 18th century in Eastern Europe, Hasidism is a branch of Orthodox Judaism that celebrates spirituality and joy. Yitzhak Buxbaum, teacher and storyteller writes: "The rebbes asked and answered such questions as: What is the place of storytelling among spiritual practices? Why do stories captivate and charm us? How should they be listened to and told? What effects do they have? That the rebbes reflected on storytelling this way undoubtedly shows its great importance in Hasidism."

Rabbi Levi Yitzhak of Berdichev's grandchild married the grandchild of the famous rebbe, Rabbi Schneur Zalman of Liadi. "Now that we are related by this marriage," said Rabbi Schneur Zalman, "let us join in performing a good deed. An innocent Jew is being held by the local authorities. Let us take up a collection, to give the officials the sum they demand for his release."

"Excellent idea," said Rabbi Levi Yitzhak. "But I ask one condition. Let us accept whatever donation is offered to us, no matter how small."

The two men went door to door. Two such distinguished rabbis seldom visited these townspeople together, so most gave generously. At last, the two rabbis came to the home of a wealthy man. He greeted them politely, then reached in his pocket, drawing out a mere half-penny. To Rabbi Schneur Zalman's horror, Rabbi Levi Yitzhak thanked the man warmly, blessed him, and turned to leave.

When Rabbi Schneur Zalman had followed his companion outside, he could contain himself no longer.

"Why should we accept that insultingly small amount from one who has so much?"

Rabbi Levi Yitzhak said, as they walked on, "I asked you to accept whatever we were given. Please be patient."

Some time later, the rich man strode up behind them. "I am sorry," he said. "Please accept more from me." He gave them a silver coin, then turned and left.

Rabbi Levi Yitzhak called after him, "You are a good and generous man!" Rabbi Schneur Zalman fumed at Rabbi Levi Yitzhak. "He could afford a hundred times as much! Why must we bless this stinginess?"

"Please bear with me, honored relative."

They continued walking.

A short while later, the rich man caught up to them again. Out of breath, he said, "Will you forgive me for how little I gave you?" He held out a sack bulging with a hundred silver coins.

Rabbi Levi Yitzhak took the rich man's hand. "Yes, with all my heart," he said. The rich man gave the coins and left, obviously relieved.

Now Levi Yitzhak turned to Rabbi Schneur Zalman. "May I tell you the story of that wealthy man? He has always given generously to those in need. But a week ago, a beggar approached him while he was meeting with a group of businessmen. Reluctant to interrupt the others to get his purse, the wealthy man reached into his pocket and gave the beggar the only coin he found there, a half-penny. The beggar was furious. This rich man was famous for giving silver coins. Why had he slighted him? The beggar threw the coin at the rich man, striking him in the face. In his pain, the wealthy man vowed to stop being so generous. From now on, he would give everyone a half-penny—no more!

"It is said that each step downward leads to another, honored relative. He was within his rights to offer the beggar only what he had. But he erred when he treated others the same way. Since that day, every one who approached him has angrily refused his paltry half-penny gifts. He found himself unable to offer more. It is also said that each step upward leads to another. Once we accepted his half-penny, we loosened the stopper on his generosity. Each gift he gave made the next one possible. Now, our willingness to receive has restored him to his goodness."

❈ ❈ ❈

STORY CIRCLE PRACTICE

REFLECTIVE QUESTIONS

❦ *How does it feel to have our offerings (of time, attention, love, resources) received warmly?*

❦ *How does it feel to have them dismissed or minimized?*

❦ *Is there a gift that is being offered to you right now that you may have overlooked?*

STORYTELLING

❦ *Where do we learn the generosity of receiving?*

Tell a story about a time when you were able to receive what was offered.

Tell a story about a time when the gift you gave was warmly accepted.

A Drum

HINDI

Indian folktales often reflect the Hindu doctrine of karma, in which human action leads to certain results, depending on the moral quality of the deed. Intention plays an important role in the outcome of any action. An act of kindness or generosity, done without any expectation of return, or reward, will yield a completely different result from one that is performed with the express purpose of getting something back.

A poor woman had only one son. She worked hard cleaning houses and grinding grain for the well-to-do families in town. They gave her some grain in return and she lived on it. But she could never afford to buy nice clothes or toys for her son. Once, when she was going to market with some grain to sell, she asked her son, "What can I bring you from the market?" He promptly replied, "A drum, Mother, get me a drum."

The mother knew she would never have enough money to buy a drum for her son. She went to the market, sold the grain, and bought some gram flour and some salt. She felt sad that she was coming home empty-handed. So when she saw a nice piece of wood on the road, she picked it up and brought it home to her son. The son didn't know what to do with it.

Yet he carried it with him when he went out to play. An old woman was lighting her *chulha*, her woodstove, with some cow-dung patties. The fire was not catching and there was smoke all around and it made the old woman's eyes water. The boy stopped and asked why she was crying. She said that she couldn't light her fire and cook. The boy said, "I have a nice piece of wood and you

can start your fire with it." The old woman was very pleased, lit the fire, made some bread, and gave a piece to the boy.

He took the bread and walked on till he came upon a potter's wife. Her child was crying and flailing his arms. The boy stopped and asked her why the child was crying. The potter's wife said the child was hungry and she had nothing in the house to give him. The boy gave the bread in his hand to the hungry child, who ate it eagerly and stopped crying. The potter's wife was grateful to the boy and gave him a pot.

When he walked on, he came to the river, where he saw a washerman and his wife quarreling. The boy stopped and asked the man why he was scolding and beating his wife. The washerman said, "This woman broke the only pot we had. Now I've nothing to boil my clothes in before I wash them." The boy said, "Here, don't quarrel, take this pot and use it." The washerman was very happy to get a large pot. He gave the boy a coat in return.

The boy walked on. He soon came to a bridge, where he saw a man shivering in the cold without so much as a shirt on him. He asked the man what had happened to his shirt, and the man said, "I was coming to the city on this horse. Robbers attacked me and took everything, even my shirt." The boy said, "Don't worry. You can have this coat." The man took the coat and said, "You're very kind, and I want to give you this horse."

The boy took the horse, and very soon he ran into a wedding party with the musicians, the bridegroom, and his family, but all of them were sitting under a tree with long faces. The boy stopped and asked why they looked so depressed. The bridegroom's father said, "We're all set to go in a wedding procession. But we need a horse for the bridegroom. The man who was supposed to bring it hasn't arrived. The bridegroom can't arrive on foot. It's getting late, and we'll miss the auspicious hour for the wedding." So the boy offered them his horse, and they were delighted. When the bridegroom asked him what he could do in return, the boy said, "You can give me something: that drum your musician is carrying." The bridegroom had no trouble persuading the drummer to give the drum to the boy. The drummer knew he could easily buy another with the money he was going to get.

The boy now rushed home to his mother, beating his new drum, and told her how he got it, beginning with a piece of wood from the roadside.

STORY CIRCLE PRACTICE

REFLECTIVE QUESTIONS

§ *Where is generosity present in this story?*

§ *How is noticing an act of generosity?*

§ *Why do we often stop noticing?*

STORYTELLING

§ *What gift have you received that you are now passing along?*

Tell a story.

The Chief of the Well

Creole is the language spoken by the majority of the population in Haiti. A mixture of French, Spanish, and other languages, Haitian Creole is rich in imagery and proverbs. Proverbs reveal the common-sense wisdom of the Haitian people, commenting on every aspect of life:

Ròch nan dlo pa konnen mizè ròch nan solèy
Rocks in the water don't know the misery of rocks in the sun.

Kreyol pale, kreyol komprann
Speak plainly, don't try to deceive.

There was once a drought in the country. The streams dried up and the wells went dry. There was no place for anybody to get water. The animals met to discuss the situation—the cow, the dog, the goat, the horse, the donkey, and all the others. They decided to ask God for help. Together they went to God and told him how bad things were.

God thought, then he said, "Don't bother your heads. They don't call me God for nothing. I will give you one well for everyone to use."

The animals thanked God. They told him he was very considerate. God said, "But you'll have to take good care of my well. One of you will have to be caretaker. He will stay by the well at all times to see that no one abuses it or makes it dirty."

Mabouya, the ground lizard, spoke up saying, "I will be caretaker."

God looked at all the animals. He said at last, "Mabouya, the lizard, looks like the best caretaker. There-fore, I appoint him. He will be the watchman. The well is over there in the mango grove."

The animals went away. The lizard went directly to the well. When the other animals began to come back for water, Mabouya challenged them. First the cow came to drink. The lizard sang out in a deep voice:

"*Qui est là?* Who's there? *Qui est là?* Who's there?
Who is walking in my grove?"

The cow replied:

"*C'est moi, la vache.* It is I, the cow,
I am coming for water. *J'ai soif.*"

And the lizard called back:

"*Va t-en!* Go away! This is God's grove,
And the well is dry."

So the cow went away and suffered from thirst.

When the horse came the lizard challenged him, saying:

"*Qui est là?* Who's there? *Qui est là?* Who's there?
Who is walking in my grove?"

The horse answered:

"*C'est moi, le cheval.* It is I, the horse,
I am coming for water. *J'ai soif.*"

And the lizard called back:

"*Va-t-en!* Go away! This is God's grove,
And the well is dry."

So the horse went away and he too suffered from thirst.

Each animal came to the well and the lizard challenged all of them in the same way, saying: "*Va-t-en!* Go away! This is God's grove,
And the well is dry."

So the animals went away and suffered much because they had no water to drink.

When God saw all the suffering going on, he said, "I gave the animals a well to drink from, but they are all dying of thirst. What is the matter? *Qu'est-ce qui se passe?*" And he himself went to the well. When the lizard heard God's footsteps, he called out:

"*Qui est là?* Who's there? *Qui est là?* Who's there?
Who is walking in my grove?"

God answered:

"*C'est moi, Papa Dieu.* It is I, Papa God.
I am coming for water. *J'ai soif.*"

And the lizard said:

"*Va-t-en, Papa Dieu.* Go away, Papa God.
The well is dry."

God was very angry. He said once more:

"*C'est moi, Papa Dieu*. It is I, Papa God.

I am coming for water. *J'ai soif.*"

And the lizard called back to him again:

"*Va-t-en, Papa Dieu*. Go away, Papa God.

The well is dry."

God spoke no more to the lizard. He sent for the animals to come to the well. He said, "You came to me because you were thirsty and I gave you a well. I made Mabouya the caretaker. But he gave no thought to the suffering creatures all around him. If a man has a banana tree in his garden, it is his. But if a man has a well in his garden, only the hole in the ground belongs to him. The water is God's and belongs to all the creatures. Because Mabouya, the lizard, became drunk with conceit, he is no longer the caretaker. From now on, he must drink his water from puddles wherever the rain falls. The new caretaker will be the frog. The frog will not say, 'Go away, the well is dry.' She will say, 'This is God's well; this is God's well.'"

So the animals drank at the well, while Mabouya, the lizard went away from it and drank rainwater wherever he could find it. The frog is now the caretaker. And all night she calls out:

"This is God's well! *Venez boire.*

This is God's well! *Venez boire.*"

And it is a saying among the people:

"The hole in the ground is yours,

But the water is God's and belongs to all the creatures."

STORY CIRCLE PRACTICE

REFLECTIVE QUESTIONS

§ *What is the difference between a caretaker and a gatekeeper?*

§ *What motivates the gatekeepers? What motivates the caretakers?*

§ *To whom do resources belong?*

STORYTELLING

§ *When have you found yourself in the role of caretaker of certain resources? How did you feel about that responsibility?*

Tell a story.

A Story and a Song

INDIA

In the classical literature of India, the recitation of certain texts is done with specific results in mind. The text is recited for the prosperity of the family, to propitiate a god, or for good health and happiness. In the case of this folktale, however, the story itself must be placated through its telling, otherwise it will take its revenge. The story warns us that traditions are meant to be kept alive, not to be hoarded in secret.

A housewife knew a story. She also knew a song. But she kept them to herself, never told anyone the story or sang the song. Imprisoned within her, the story and the song were feeling choked. They wanted release, wanted to run away. One day, when the woman was sleeping with her mouth open, the story escaped, fell out of her, took the shape of a pair of shoes, and sat outside the house. The song also escaped, took the shape of something like a man's coat, and hung on a peg.

The woman's husband came home, looked at the coat and shoes, and asked her, "Who's visiting?"

"No one," she said.

"But whose coat and shoes are these?"

"I don't know," she replied.

He wasn't satisfied with her answer. He was suspicious. Their conversation was unpleasant. The unpleasantness led to a quarrel. The husband flew into a rage, picked up his blanket, and went to the Monkey God's temple to sleep.

The woman didn't understand what was happening. She lay down alone that night. She asked the same question over and over: "Whose coat and shoes are these?" Baffled and unhappy, she put out the lamp and went to sleep.

All the lamp flames of the town, once they were put out, used to come to the Monkey God's temple and spend the night there, gossiping. On this night, all the lamps of all the houses were represented there—all except one, which came late.

The others asked the latecomer, "Why are you so late tonight?"

"At our house, the couple quarreled late into the night," said the flame.

"Why did they quarrel?"

"When the husband wasn't home, a pair of shoes came onto the verandah, and a man's coat somehow got onto a peg. The husband asked her whose they were. The wife said she didn't know. So they quarreled."

"Where did the coat and shoes come from?"

"The lady of our house," said the flame, "knows a story and a song. She never tells the story, and has never sung the song to anyone. The story and the song got suffocated inside; so they got out and have turned into a coat and a pair of shoes. They took revenge. The woman doesn't even know."

The husband, lying under his blanket in the temple, heard the lamp's explanation. His suspicions were cleared. When he went home, it was dawn. He asked his wife about her story and her song. But she had forgotten them. "What story, what song?" she said.

❋ ❋ ❋

STORY CIRCLE PRACTICE

REFLECTIVE QUESTIONS

§ *What happens to the gifts that never get expressed?*

§ *What conditions allow us to tell our story and sing our song?*

§ *Is there a story or a song you are ready to share with the world?*

STORYTELLING

Tell a story about a time when you took a risk and shared your gifts.

The Origin of Water Animals

Thousands of megalithic monuments can be found scattered over Nagaland, the mountainous state in northeastern India populated by distinct tribal peoples called the Naga. These standing stones are a vital part of Naga culture. They line the approaches to villages or the paths that wind past abandoned village-sites, standing in pairs or in long double-rows. Wealthy men have set them up to commemorate their fame and generosity, and to enhance the fertility of their fields.

Once upon a time a crab, a frog, a shrimp, and a minnow were friends. All four were females and they worked together very well. Each helped the others by doing what she could do best. Each day at dinnertime they arranged a fine meal and ate together. Like humans, these animals grew rice. They worked as a group in one another's fields, thus making the work more enjoyable, due to the company. The four took turns cooking. The one whose turn it was to cook would leave the field early and go home to prepare dinner. When it was ready she would call her friends from the fields, asking them to join her.

After a while it was agreed that the crab's cooking was the best. So, they asked the crab if she would cook every day. She would be delighted to, she said, and thereafter this was her job. One day, there was no meat available to make a decent meal. So the crab took off one of her own legs and added it to the vegetables. When the meal was ready she called her friends as usual. They thought the meal was especially good that day and helped themselves to extra portions. They praised the crab for sacrificing her leg and making such a good meal, even in time of want.

The crab was so pleased with the praise she received from her friends that she continued to remove one after another of her legs each day. She put each leg into the curry until only the stump of her body remained. Each day the group praised her again for her cooking and urged her to continue in her role as chef. She gladly accepted, because their praise warmed her heart.

One day, while the group of three friends was working in the field they realized it was already past time for their midday meal. Still they waited patiently for the crab to call them to dinner. But there was no call. Eventually they decided to go home anyway. But the crab was not at the house. The friends called for her but there was no answer. They decided that she must have returned to the river to bathe or perhaps grow new legs. They were hungry and so they decided to eat without waiting for her. It was already quite late. As they opened the curry pot to serve their food, there was the crab's body right in the middle of the curry, flavoring the whole dish with her tasty meat.

Seeing the sacrifice the crab had made of herself, the other three animals all started to laugh. They laughed and laughed until they couldn't stand up straight. They laughed until they rolled around on the floor. They laughed until evening, when they finally stopped from sheer exhaustion. When the frog tried to get up, however, she could no longer stand erect. Her back had become permanently bent at the base of the spine from laughing so hard. The fish's neck had become so swollen that it no longer had the graceful curves it used to have. Now it was stiff and straight. The shrimp could no longer walk forward, but only backward as she had been doing during her fit of laughter. Unable to continue their work in the fields, all these animals took to the water. And that is where we find them today.

❈ ❦ ❈

STORY CIRCLE PRACTICE

REFLECTIVE QUESTIONS

~ *Is there a danger in being praised for our generosity?*

~ *Do people have different capacities for giving?*

~ *How do we view acts of sacrifice in our culture?*

STORYTELLING:

~ *Who are our role models for giving? What did we learn from them?*

Tell a story about an individual whose generosity appeared boundless.

Tell a story about your own journey with giving.

THREE

WORKING TOGETHER

In all these scenes of animal life that crossed before my eyes, I saw mutual aid and mutual support carried on to an extent which made me suspect in it a feature of the greatest importance for the maintenance of life, the preservation of each species and its further evolution.[11]

—PETER KROPOTKIN

E ach of the stories in this section reveals a particular aspect of working together towards a common goal—practice, mutual respect, and having a shared vision. It all begins with practice. In the first story, a Jataka tale retold by Rafe Martin, the wise quail encourages his fellow quail to go deeper into the forest and practice working together. He knows that without practice conflict is likely. But what does this kind of practice look like in practical terms? In a dance company, an orchestra, or a hockey team, it means being attentive and responsive to others. It means being willing to contribute to the whole without concern for personal recognition. Discipline, patience, and compassion are nurtured in the process of collaboration. A beautiful example of the benefits of this kind of teamwork comes from South America: In 1975, Venezuelan music director José Antonio Abreu founded El Sistema ("the system") to help poor Venezuelan kids learn to play a musical instrument and be part of an orchestra. Since then, El Sistema has seeded 102 youth orchestras, as well as many happy lives. Abreu explains how this works: "In its essence, the orchestra and the choir are much more than artistic structures: they are examples and schools of social life because to sing and to play together means to intimately co-exist toward perfection and excellence, following a strict discipline of coordination and organization in order to seek the harmonic

---

11   Peter Kropotkin, *Mutual Aid.* (Montreal: Black Rose Books, 1989).

interdependence of voice and instruments."[12] While we may not strive for the kind of harmony necessary to musical performance, any form of collaboration will ask us to "play together" with mutual respect and appreciation.

The second story, another Jataka tale, features three very different animals. Here we see how these qualities of mutual interest and concern for the others' well-being lead to a successful outcome. Knowing what each other's gifts are and inviting one's partners to bring them forward creates an atmosphere of creative engagement. This is one of the lessons my listeners in Mississippi took from the story. Sometimes, however, we need the wisdom of a third party to take stock of our dilemma and advise us. In "The Friendship Orchard", a Kazakh folktale retold by Pleasant deSpain, two friends argue over a chest of gold, each insisting that the other keep it. The elder to whom they go for advice listens carefully to their quandary. After hearing the story of their friendship he presents an alternative use for the gold. Rather than suggesting one or the other keep it, he proposes that they use the money to leave a legacy. This is what the philosopher Marcus Aurelius calls the "view from above" that is, the ability to see the bigger perspective, the long-term potential of our actions. Working together in friendship and mutual appreciation we can achieve so much more than when we remain isolated from each other. But it takes practice. And the storytelling circle is a wonderful place to start, since its success depends on the participation and presence of everyone in the circle.

---

12 Abreu, Jose Antonio. (2009, February). "Jose Antonio Abreu: The El Sistema music revolution." 2009. TedTalk. [Video file]. Retrieved from http://www.ted.com/talks/lang/en/jose_abreu_on_kids_transformed_by_music.html

The Wise Quail

INDIA

One of the oldest story collections in the world comes from the Buddhist tradition. The Jataka tales are said to be the Buddha's recollection of his former lives. In each of these tales, the Buddha-to-be is born as a human, an animal or a tree spirit. In each tale we see him developing qualities such as generosity, wisdom, patience, and loving-kindness, all of which come into play in this story.

Once, the Buddha was a wise quail, the leader of a flock. One day, a hunter came into the forest. Imitating the quails' own calls, he began to trap unwary birds. The wise quail noticed that something was amiss. Calling his flock together, he announced, "My fellow quail, I am afraid that there is a hunter in our forest. Many of our brothers and sisters are missing. We must be alert. Danger is all around us. Still, if we work together we can stay free. Please listen to my plan. If you should hear a whistling call—twe whee! twe whee! twe whee!—as if a brother or sister were calling, be very watchful! If you follow that call, you may find darkness descending upon you. Your wings may be pinned so that you cannot fly, and the fear of death may grip your heart. If these things happen, just understand that you have been trapped by the hunter's net and do not give up! Remember, if you work together you can be free.

"Now, this is my plan. You must stick your heads out through the webs of the net and, then, you must all flap your wings together. As a group, though you are still bound in the net, you will rise up into the air. Fly to a bush. Let the net drape on the branches of the bush so you can each drop to the ground, and fly away from under the net, this way and that, to freedom. Do you understand? Can you do this?"

"We do understand," answered all the quail as one, "and we will do it! We will work together and be free."

Hearing this, the wise quail was content. The very next day a group of quail were pecking on the ground when they heard a long whistling call. "Twe whee! twe whee! twe whee!" It was the cry of a quail in distress! Off they rushed. Suddenly darkness descended on them and their wings were pinned. They had indeed been trapped by the hunter's net. But, remembering the wise quail's words, they did not panic. Sticking their heads out through the webs of the net they flapped their wings together, harder and harder, and slowly, slowly, with the net still draped upon them, they rose, as a group, through the air. They flew to a bush. They dropped down through the bush, leaving the net hung on the outer branches, then flew away, each in their own direction, this way and that, to freedom.

The plan had worked! They were safe! They had escaped from the jaws of death. And, oh, they were happy!

But the hunter was not happy. He could not understand how the quail had escaped him. And this happened not just once, but many times. At last, the hunter realized the truth. "Why," he said, amazed, "those quail are cooperating! They are working together! But it can't last. They are only birds, featherbrains after all. Sooner or later they will argue. And when they do, I shall have them." And so, he was patient.

Now, the wise quail had had the same thought. Sooner or later the birds of his flock would begin to argue, and when that happened they would be lost. So he decided to take them deeper into the forest, far from their present danger.

That very day something happened to confirm the wise quail's thought. A quail was pecking on the ground for seeds when another bird of the flock, descending rapidly, accidentally struck it with its wing-tip. "Hey! Watch it, stupid!" called the first quail, in anger.

"Stupid is it?" responded the newly-landed quail, flustered because he had been careless, "Why are you so high and mighty? You were too dumb to move out of my way! Yes, you were too dumb, you dumb cluck!"

"Dumb cluck is it?" cried the first quail, "Dumb cluck? Why, talking of dumb, it's clear that you can't even land without slapping someone in the face! If that isn't 'dumb,' I don't know what is! Who taught you to fly anyway—the naked-winged bats?"

"Bats is it?" yelled the second quail, enraged, "Bats? Why, I'll give you a bat, you feathered ninny!" And with a loud chirruping whistle he hurled himself straight at the other quail. Chasing furiously after one another, loudly hurling insults and threats back and forth, they flew, twisting and turning, between the great, silent trees of the grove. An argument had started and, as is the way of arguments, no end was in sight.

The wise quail was nearby and he heard it all. At once he knew that danger was again upon them. If they could not work together the hunter was sure to have them. So again he called his flock together and said, "My dear brother and sister quail. The hunter is here. Let us go elsewhere, deeper into the forest and there, in seclusion, discipline ourselves, practicing our skills in working together. In this way we shall become truly free from the danger."

Many of the birds said, "Though we love our present home, we shall go with you, Wise Quail. The danger is great and we wish to find safety."

But others said, "Why go from this pleasant spot? You yourself, Wise Quail, have taught us all we need to know in order to be free. We know what to do. We just have to stick our heads out, flap our wings together, and fly away. Any dumb cluck can do it! We're going to stay."

So some of the birds flew off with the wise quail, while the others stayed. A few days later, while some of those who stayed were scratching around for their dinner, they heard a whistling call. "Twe whee! twe whee! twe whee!" They ran to answer the call when suddenly, darkness descended upon them. Fear gripped their hearts. They were trapped in the hunter's net! But, remembering the wise quail's teaching, they stuck their heads through the net, and one bird said, "On the count of three we all flap. Ready? One two, three."

"Hey!" called another bird, "Who made you boss? Who said you could give the orders?"

"I'm the hardest worker and the strongest," said the first bird. "When I flap my wings, the dust rises from the earth and whirls up in clouds. Without me you'd never get this net off the ground. So I give the orders, see?"

"No, I don't see!" shouted another bird. "What you've just described is nothing. Why, when I flap my wings, all the leaves move on the trees, the branches bend and even the trunks sway. That's how strong I am. So if anyone should be giving orders around here it's me!"

"No, me!" shouted a third bird.

"Me!" yelled a fourth.

"No! No! Listen to me!" screamed the first bird again above the rising din. "Flap Flap! Flap! I tell you. Flap your wings all together when I say 'three!'"

But no one flapped. They just argued and argued. And as they argued, the hunter came along and found them and their fate, alas, was not a happy one. But the quail who had gone off deeper into the safety of the great forest learned, under the wise quail's guidance, how to really cooperate. They practiced constantly, until they were, indeed, able to work together without anger or argument. Though the hunter tried many times to catch them he never could. And if he never caught them, why, they're still free today.

※ ❧ ※

STORY CIRCLE PRACTICE

ॐ *How do we practice working together?*

ॐ *What role does our style of communication play in creating a positive environment for collaboration?*

STORYTELLING

Tell a story about an experience of working cooperatively with others.

ॐ *Have you had the experience of being encouraged to share your particular gifts? How did that feel?*

Tell a story.

The Antelope, the Woodpecker, and the Turtle

INDIA

In Pali, the language of the earliest Buddhist teach-
ings, the word for loving-kindness is metta, which
is also translated as unconditional friendliness. The
practice of metta or loving-kindness involves system-
atically extending goodwill to various beings, begin-
ning with oneself and moving through such catego-
ries as benefactor and dear friend to difficult person
and then to all beings in all directions. This beauti-
ful practice orients the heart to the good in ourselves
and in others. It reminds us that friendship is more
than just connecting. It is life-sustaining.

Once, in the past, the Buddha-to-be was born as an antelope—Kurunga-miga. He lived in a thicket in the middle of the woods, by a lake.

At the top of a tree by that very same lake there lived a wood-pecker—Satapatto. And in the lake, there lived a turtle—Kacchapo. The antelope, the woodpecker, and the turtle were friends. They lived together and they took care of each other.

How did they take care of each other? Well, they told each other stories. The woodpecker's stories were short, and to the point. They went like this: "Da, da-da. Da, da-da, da, da." The turtle's stories, on the other hand, were slow and ponderous. They went on and on, and on, until sometimes, the woodpecker and the antelope fell asleep. The stories told by the antelope, on the other hand, spoke of things he had seen in the forest—creatures living their lives, teaching their young how to be in the world. Somehow, whenever the antelope told one of his stories, the wood-pecker and the turtle felt a little kinder, and a little wiser.

One day a hunter entered the forest. He happened to see the hoof-prints of the antelope in the soft earth by the edge of the lake, where Kurunga-miga went to drink each night. The hunter laid a snare. It was made of leather, but it was strong as an iron chain. Then he went away. That night, when Kurunga-miga came to drink, his leg was caught in the snare. He cried out in fear.

Down from the top of the tree flew Satapatto, the woodpecker. Out from the water of the lake climbed Kacchapo, the turtle. They looked and saw their friend the antelope, with his hind-leg trapped in the snare, trembling and frightened.

"What can we do?" said Kacchapo, his wet shell gleaming in the moonlight.

"I know," said Satapatto. "You have a beak, Kacchapo. Use your beak. Chew and cut this leather snare. I will fly through the woods to the hunter's lodge. I will slow the hunter and prevent him from coming at first light."

Kacchapo sat down and began to cut and chew the snare.

Khadati, khadati, khadati.

Khadati, khadati, khadati.

As he chewed Kurunga-miga, the antelope, murmured the turtle's name to encourage him.

He said, "Kacchapo. Kacchapo. Kacchapo."

Meanwhile Satapatto, the woodpecker, flew through the woods. The sound of his wings lifting and falling made a sound, like the sound of his own name:

Satapatto, Satapatto, Satapatto.

Satapatto, Satapatto, Satapatto.

He flew through the forest, right to the hunter's lodge. There he alighted in a tree, and waited for any sound of the hunter preparing to set out. When light first showed in the east he heard the hunter moving about. Inside the lodge, the hunter slung his leather pouch over one shoulder. He took his knife in one hand. Then he opened the door. At that very moment Satapatto cried out, flew down from the tree, flapped his wings, and struck the hunter in the face. The hunter was amazed.

"What is this black-winged bird of evil omen?" He turned about, shut the door, and went back to bed. This was not a good way to start the day.

The hunter said to himself, "This bird of evil omen struck me in the face when I went through the front door. Now I'll go by the back door."

But Satapatto, waiting in the tree, thought to himself, "This hunter came out by the front door. The second time he'll go by the back door."

Satapatto flew to the rear of the hunter's lodge. He alighted in a tree and waited.

When the hunter opened the door and stepped out Satapatto flew down from the tree, flapped his wings, and struck the hunter in the face.

The hunter was astonished. "This bird does not want me to set out!"

He turned about and shut the door.

Now he waited until the sun began to climb over the treetops, into the sky.

Then, thinking of what he might have caught in his leather snare, he took up his knife and his pouch, opened the door, and crouching low, he went quickly along the forest trails towards the lake.

Satapatto flew ahead of him to warn the antelope and the turtle. His wings went up and down, even more quickly than before.

Satapatto, Satapatto, Satapatto.

Satapatto, Satapatto, Satapatto.

He flew through the woods to the edge of the lake, where Kurunga-miga, the antelope, was caught in the hunter's snare.

"The hunter is coming! The hunter is coming!" warned the woodpecker.

All night long the turtle had cut and chewed the snare. His beak was broken. There was blood at the edges of his mouth. He was weak and exhausted. But only one thin strand of the leather snare remained.

"The hunter is coming!" warned Satapatto.

Kurunga-miga looked and saw the hunter coming with his knife. He snapped the leather snare and went running down the trail. The woodpecker flew up into a tree, and when the hunter arrived, there was no antelope in his snare, but there, at the edge of the lake, was a beautiful turtle, with a beautiful turtle shell. He picked up Kacchapo and put him in his leather pouch.

As he ran down the trail, Kurunga-miga looked back. He saw that his friend Kacchapo had been seized. He said to himself, "I will save my friend." He came back a little ways on the trail. He pretended to stumble. He made sure that the hunter could see him.

The hunter did see him. "This little antelope is weak," he said. "I will catch him easily." He unslung the leather pouch and set it on the ground. Then he set off after the antelope.

Kurunga-miga led the hunter this way and that way on the forest trails, never letting him come too close, but never letting him stray too far behind. He led him right to the other side of the lake. Then he summoned all his strength and came leaping and jumping, swift as the wind, right back to the spot where Kacchapo was trapped in the leather pouch. He crouched down low and caught the pouch on his two sharp, pointed horns. He lifted it up and let it fall. The pouch split open, and out stepped Kacchapo.

Then down from the tree flew Satapatto and alighted on the ground.

Kurunga-miga spoke to the turtle and the woodpecker: "My friends," he said, "Kacchapo, Satapatto. You have done for me what ought to be done by a friend. You have given me my life. Now, quickly, before the hunter returns, Satapatto, take your young ones and fly through the woods to safety. And you, Kacchapo, hide yourself in the waters of the lake, where the hunter will not see you. And I will run and hide in the thicket."

They each went their separate ways, and when the hunter came back he found only a broken snare and a torn pouch. He looked closely and saw the hoof-prints of the antelope, drops of blood from the turtle's beak, and one black wing-feather. There, on the forest floor, he read the story of their friendship.

"This feather, could it be from the bird that struck me in the face this very morning?" he asked himself. "And this snare, see how it has been cut and chewed. Could it be that the turtle used his sharp beak to cut the snare and release the antelope? And these hoof-prints returning . . . did the antelope come back to rescue the turtle?"

He was amazed, and shaking his head in disbelief, he gathered up the torn pouch and the broken snare. He set off, disappointed and discouraged, but hoping that next time he might catch some creatures who didn't have such good friends.

※ ※ ※

STORY CIRCLE PRACTICE

REFLECTIVE QUESTIONS

§ *How do the stories you tell resemble you?*

§ *What is the role of friendship in your life?*

STORYTELLING

§ *What does it feel like to have our gifts and skills recognized by another?*

Tell a story about being seen. Tell a story about inviting a friend to step into his or her gifts.

The Friendship Orchard

CENTRAL ASIA—KAZAKHSTAN

Storytelling plays a particularly important role in nomadic cultures, where oral traditions are the primary means of passing along values and shared history. In Central Asia, the akyns are the improvising poets and singers in the Kazakh and Kyrgz cultures. Akyns improvise in the form of a song-like recitation to the accompaniment of a stringed instrument known as the dombra (among Kazakhs) or a qomoz (among Krgyz). In pre-Soviet times, akyns gave voice to people's thoughts and feelings, exposing social vices, and glorifying heroes.

Two elderly friends tilled a small patch of earth on the barren steppe. They raised vegetables and a few sheep, but life was hard and they earned little. Winter was especially difficult because of the dreaded snowstorms known as *dzhut*, in which previously thawed snow froze over. Sheep couldn't dig though the ice for food and often perished. Because they were old and poor, they took care to watch out for one another. One of the men was named Kurai. He owned the land on which they lived and worked. The other was called Dau, and he was in charge of the sheep.

One winter, a severe *dzhut* struck their farm. Soon after, all their sheep starved to death. Dau took Kurai aside and said, "My life has ended. I'll wander into the hills and let the storms take me as well. You've been a fine friend, Kurai. I will miss you."

"No, no, Dau," replied Kurai. "You can't go off and leave me. Who will help with the garden, come spring? Who will tell me stories around the night fire? I want you here, on the land with me. I'm giving you half ownership of the field. You take the lower half, and I'll keep the upper part. The deed is already in your name."

A rare and wonderful thing happened the following spring. Dau was digging in his half of the field and struck something made of metal with his hoe. He dug deeper into the black earth and uncovered a small, iron chest. It was filled with gold coins. He ran to Kurai, shouting, "You are rich! You can live like a kahn. And you deserve it, Kurai, for you are a good man."

Kurai said, "You found the gold in your half of the field, Dau. The treasure is yours, and yours alone. I'm truly happy for you."

"No, my generous friend," explained Dau. "The gold is yours. You have given me my life. How can I take anything more?"

"God has given you the gold," said Kurai.

"How can I take from God that which He has given to you?"

"Enough of your stubbornness!" cried Dau. "Take the gold."

"Enough of your nonsense!" replied Kurai. "The gold is yours."

The two friends argued long into the night. Neither gave in to the other. They were exhausted by morning and decided to talk with a teacher who lived in the middle of the steppes. He was known as the wisest man in the region. It took five days to find the wise man's hut. The two friends showed him the gold and told him of their argument. The teacher looked at the coins and then at the men. He looked again at the coins and again at the men. Then he closed his eyes and thought and thought. After a long while, he opened his eyes and said, "Take the gold to the city and buy the highest quality seeds in the land. Return to your fields and plant the finest orchard in the steppes. Make it an orchard of friendship. Allow the poor to rest in its shade, eat of its fruit, and enjoy its beauty. Rather than divide two friends, let the gold serve many."

Kurai and Dau agreed, and left for the city. They arrived several days later and headed for the marketplace. They searched and searched for a seller of fruit seeds, but had no luck. No one had seeds to sell. The old men were tired and decided to rest for the night and try again the following day. On the way to an inn, they heard a terrible screeching coming from a thousand caged birds, carried by a caravan of camels. The colorful birds had been captured in the thick forests and high mountains, and were being taken to market. They would be sold as food for wealthy tables.

Kurai looked at Dau and said, "It isn't good to be put in a cage." Dau looked at Kurai and said, "It isn't right that beautiful birds should be eaten by the rich." They approached the leader of the caravan and asked the price of the birds. He looked at their poor clothes and said, "More than you have."

Kurai opened the iron chest. "Release them and the gold is yours," he said. Dau nodded his head in agreement. The leader ordered his helpers to set the birds free. Up into the sky they flew, singing songs of joy! Kurai and Dau began their long walk home, feeling happy for the birds, but sad for the orchard that would never be. They talked about their long friendship and decided that it was foolish to argue.

Arriving home a few days later, they witnessed a strange sight.

A thousand beautiful birds sat in their field and scratched in the dirt. Each held a seed in its beak and dropped it into the loose soil. The dirt was smoothed over the seeds with the beating of strong wings. Then, creating a multicolored cloud of feather and song, the birds rose into the sky and flew away. Rain fell and the seeds sprouted, climbing slowly from earth toward sky. The orchard took root. Apple trees and pear trees and apricot, too. Trees take time to grow, and the two old men passed on before they could taste the first of the fruit. Kurai and Dau were not saddened, however, as they had eaten from the fruit of friendship for so many years.

❈ ❦ ❈

STORY CIRCLE PRACTICE

REFLECTIVE QUESTIONS

§ *How does friendship leave a legacy?*

§ *Do you see examples of this in your life?*

STORYTELLING

Tell a story of someone whose example has inspired you to make a difference in the world.

FOUR

BECOMING A LEADER

To promote the recovery of our world and the healing of our communities, while also leading lives that are rich and satisfying, we need to embody a larger story of who and what we are.[13]

—JOANNA MACY

W hat does it mean to be a leader in the twenty-first century? Where do we look for true leadership? World folklore takes delight in poking at the vanity and conceit of leaders while presenting as powerful role models those without position or wealth. Good leaders are all around us. The qualities they embody have much to do with compassion and wisdom. The four stories in this section reflect the presence of these qualities in successful leadership. In the first story, "The Clever Sheik of the Butana," we see how leadership encompasses generosity when there is room for mercy. In addition to forgiveness, the thief in the story receives a gift of money to start a new and honest life. He is welcomed into the community, rather than being banished. Generous leadership is about inclusion.

In "The Wisdom of the Crows," the king of the crows places himself in danger for the sake of his community. As he prepares to confront the human king with his unskillful action, he selects loving-kindness as his guide—this quality that sees the good in others. He knows that a leader must communicate his belief in the best in each of us.

The third story offers its lesson through the absence of generosity. In the Haitian tale, "The King of the Animals," no animals are deemed fit to be a leader. Each is found lacking in some way, because of their behavior, their appearance, or because of the work they do. As we discover, the search for a leader is more likely to be successful when it begins with appreciation.

---

13 Joanna Macy and Chris Johnstone, *Active Hope: How to Face the Mess We're in without Going Crazy.* (Novato, California: New World Library, 2012), p. 92.

In the last story, "All Things Are Connected," we are reminded that each of us is a leader when we speak truth to power and when we assert our wisdom in the face of arrogance and privilege. Leadership considers the legacy of our actions and reminds others to do the same.

In the story circle there may be a facilitator but there is not just one leader. In fact there is both a storyteller and a leader in every seat.[14] We are leading through our example in each and every interaction in our lives. There may be times, however, when we feel called upon to take initiative and assume a clear leadership role. The king of the crows makes this kind of decision when he hears the news of the slaughter of crows in the city. He says to himself, "Besides me, there is no other who can cure my kinsmen of their fear." This is not vanity but discernment. By taking that leadership role he risks his own life to save the lives of others. He enters the enemy camp and addresses the king as a peer: "I, too am a king and a great fear has been born in my people—the fear of death." He admonishes the king for too quickly accepting the advice of his high priest when he informed him that crows' fat would heal the wounds on the elephants' backs. He calls the king to account and establishes him in the precept of non-harming, challenging him to rule without violence. Wise leadership, as portrayed in this tale, rests on a foundation of generosity and compassion.

The art of leadership is really the art of listening with a wise and generous heart. The wisdom tales of the world remind us that this is possible.

---

14   See Christina Baldwin and Ann Linnea, *The Circle Way: A Leader in Every Chair*. (San Francisco: Berrett-Koehler Publishers, Inc., 2010).

The Clever Sheik of the Butana

SUDAN

Among the Dinka of Sudan cieng *(pronounced "chee-eng") is a concept which refers to appropriate conduct, care-taking, and mutual respect. In its varied meanings,* cieng *emphasizes good human relations. The goal is much more than the avoidance of conflict and violation of other people's rights; it imposes a communal obligation to foster cooperation among the people in the shaping and sharing of values. Unity and harmony as social ideals are frequently advocated in songs even as the singer boasts of his ability to use force against an opponent.*[15]

Many tents were scattered over a wide range of the Butana, that piece of land that lies east of the river known as the Blue Nile in the Sudan. The tents marked the capital of Sheik Hamad, who was the ruler of the tribes that lived in the Butana.

One day Sheik Hamad received a visitor, who was on his way to a far-off town. The traveler was hosted very generously by Sheikh Hamad, as is the custom of the Sudanese. The Sheikh slew a big ox for the visitor and asked all the people to come for supper with the traveler. They had their supper and after that they sat listening to songs of bravery and stories of how they defeated their opponents from different tribes. They listened to music played on a flute called a *zumbara*, and every tune, or *loda*, told of a certain event.

At last, in the middle of the night, the feast came to an end and the guest was taken to his tent to sleep.

In the morning, unfortunately, the guest found that his money was gone, all of it. It had been stolen. A thief had broken into the tent while the people of the tribe were honoring the guest and making the feast for him.

---

15 Deng, Francis Mading. *The Dinka and Their Songs.* (London: Oxford University Pres, 1973), p. 14-15 and p.78.

The guest told Sheik Hamad about the theft. Sheik Hamad said to him, "Don't tell anybody about this. In the evening, when all the people come to the feast, we shall get your money back."

The day passed very slowly, and the guest spent the long hours thinking about his lost money, if it was going to be returned to him, and how.

In the evening, another ox was slain for the guest and the people of the tribe. The Sheik's four wives, the women of the tribe, and the servants cooked the food. All the people were invited and all of them came.

After they had eaten, enjoyed themselves, listened to many songs and *zumbara lodas*, Sheikh Hamad stood up and addressed the people. "Well, our guest has lost all his money. Whoever took it or found it lying on the ground, let him step forward now and give it back." Nobody came forward.

Then the Sheikh said to them, "My donkey is in that tent. I want every man here to enter the tent, take hold of the donkey's tail, then come out the other entrance. Make sure you hold the tail of the donkey. If the one who holds the tail is innocent, nothing will happen to him, but when the one who has taken the money holds the tail, the donkey will bray. So go."

The first man entered and came out by the other door. Nothing happened. The second did the same. Nothing happened. The third, the fourth. But still nothing happened. Every man entered and came out, but the donkey didn't make any sound.

The Sheikh then asked the men to stand in a row and he went from one to the next. He took each man's hands, put them near his face, and then let them go. One by one he did this. Then the Sheikh took the hands of one of the men, put them near his face, very near his nose, and ordered him to step out.

He said to the man, "You have stolen the money. I want it brought now." The man tried his best to deny it, but Sheikh Hamad told him that the more he denied it, the worse his punishment would be. The Sheikh whispered in the thief's ear, "I oiled the donkey's tail with scented *dihn* oil. All the innocent people took hold of it and the scent of the *dihn* was in their palms, but, because you were afraid that the donkey might bray, you didn't hold it. And the *dihn* scent didn't get on your hands. Bring the money now, or you will curse the day on which your mother gave birth to you."

The man, accompanied by two of the Sheikh's guards went away, dug a hole in ground, and brought the money. The man promised not to do such a thing ever again. He was forgiven and was given part of the money to start a new, honest life.

❈ ❧ ❈

STORY CIRCLE PRACTICE

§ *How do we understand justice? Where do we find models of justice in our society?*

STORYTELLING:

§ *What examples come to mind when you think of generous leadership?*

Tell a story of different styles of leadership.

The Wisdom of the Crows

INDIA

In Mahayana Buddhism the term bodhicitta means "awakened mind" or "desire for enlightenment." It refers to the intention to develop qualities such as generosity and wisdom not just for oneself, but for the benefit of all beings. Regarded as a precious seed that is to be nurtured and cultivated, bodhicitta, says Tibetan teacher Tsoknyi Rinpche, "is the juice that really transforms our meditation practice from a kind of mental aerobics exercise into the profound experience of the kind that changes not only our own lives but the lives of everyone around us."[16]

Once, a very long time ago, the Buddha was born as a crow. He lived in a forest cemetery, near the ancient city of Varanasi, where King Brahmadatta ruled the kingdom. When he grew up the Bodhisatta[17] became the leader of a great company of crows.

Now it happened that early one morning, the king's high priest left Varanasi by the eastern gate and went down to the holy river Ganges to bathe. When he emerged from the water he dressed in his finest white muslin robes. He placed a garland of white jasmine flowers about his neck, and returned towards the city.

Two crows were sitting on top of the arched gates of the city. One crow spoke to the other: "My friend," he said, "I have an idea. I shall let some droppings fall on the shiny head of that Brahmin. See him coming from the river, freshly washed, in his fine robes?"

---

16 Tsoknyi Rinpoche. "A Different Discipline." Posted May 16, 2012. The Huffington Post. http://www.huffingtonpost.com/Tsoknyi-rinpoche/discipline_b_1513499.html

17 In his previous lives the Buddha is referred to as the *Bodhisatta*, which means "one on the path to awakening."

"What?" said the other crow, tilting his head in amazement. "You would do what? Please, do not amuse yourself by doing that. This Brahmin is a lord. If his anger is aroused he could cause the destruction of all the crows."

The first crow shrugged his shiny shoulders. "I can't help myself," he said. "I have to do it."

The second one replied, "Do it, then, if you must. We'll see what happens." He left the first crow sitting there and he flew away.

Sure enough, when the king's high priest arrived below the gate, that crow let some droppings fall, right on his shiny head.

The priest looked up to see the source of his humiliation—a black-winged crow, just taking flight. Anger was born in his heart, and he set himself to take revenge upon all the crows.

At that time, a serving-girl was earning her wages by guarding the rice outside the granary shed, not far from the king's elephant stables. She had spread the rice in the sun to dry, and she was sitting at the door of the hut, guarding it. The day was hot, and while she was sitting there the girl dozed off. A long-haired goat, roaming about, noticed that she was off her guard. He came up and began to nibble and chew on the rice. At the sound of his chewing, the girl woke up, and shooed him away. A second time she fell asleep, and a second time the goat returned to eat the rice. Once more the sound of his snuffling and chewing woke the girl and she chased him away. And it all happened a third time, exactly as before.

Then the girl said to herself, "This ram, nibbling again and again, will eat up half the rice. I am sure to lose my wages. I shall find a way to prevent him from ever returning again." She went to a nearby cooking fire. She took out a long smoldering stick and returned to her place by the door of the hut. She sat down and pretended to fall asleep, still holding the burning stick by one end. The goat arrived a moment later and began to nibble and chew on the rice. At the sound of his chewing the girl stood up and threw the stick. She struck the goat right on the back, where his hair was longest. Straight away the goat's long hair caught fire.

Leaping and jumping the goat ran, with his body burning, right to the elephant stables where he rolled on a pile of straw. The straw blazed up and the elephant stables caught fire. The elephants were trapped in their stalls, and before the fire could be put out, many of the elephants were wounded, with their backs badly burned.

The king's elephant doctors did what they could, but they were unable to find a remedy for the wounds on the elephants' backs. They reported this to the king. The king was very fond of his elephants and it distressed him to think of them in pain. He spoke to his high priest. He said, "Teacher, do you know any cure for the wounds on my elephants' backs?"

The king's high priest thought for a moment. "Yes, your majesty," he said. "I do."

"What is it?" asked the king.

"Crows' fat, your majesty. It is an ancient remedy. But a great many crows will have to be slaughtered to obtain enough fat for a cure."

The king was pleased. "Very well," he said. "Let the crows be killed, and their fat obtained."

On that day there began a slaughter of crows in the city. From the temple roofs, and the branches of the banyan trees the king's archers shot them down. Their black bodies tumbled and fell. Soon, there were heaps of dead crows all over the city, their ragged wings broken, their eyes open and staring. They were gathered in carts and taken to the king's kitchens where their bodies were boiled to extract the fat. So little fat was obtained to be of almost no use at all. Still, the king's orders did not change. The crows of the city were to be shot and killed—large and small, young and old, male and female. A great fear was born in the crows of Varanasi.

Now at that time, the Bodhisatta, living in his forest cemetery, was surrounded by many thousand crows. Some of these had relatives who lived in the city. One evening, a city crow arrived in the cemetery, and told the Bodhisatta what was hap-

pening. The king of the crows thought to himself: "Besides me, there is no one else who can cure my kinsmen of their fear." He flew up into a Sal tree and sat there quietly, summoning to his mind the ten perfections, reviewing each one in turn: generosity; virtue; renunciation; patience; energy; resolve; loving-kindness; truthfulness, wisdom; equanimity. He considered each of these qualities, and how they might serve him.

Then he selected loving-kindness as his guide. He flew quickly through the forest and over the walls of the city, where heaps of crows lay dead in the streets. Straight to the king's palace he flew, entering through an open window, and alighting before the king's empty seat. He climbed in beneath it and hid himself there.

A serving-man came forward to seize him, but the king, just entering the hall, said, "Let him be. Surely he is a messenger." The Bodhisatta recovered himself, and once more called up loving-kindness to be his guide. Then he came out and addressed the king.

"Great King," he said, "I, too, am a king, and a great fear has been born in my people—the fear of death. Is it not true, Your Majesty, that a king should do what ever is in his power for the well-being and safety of his people?"

The king nodded. He was greatly amazed to be addressed by a crow. The Bodhisatta, king of the crows, continued, "Your Majesty, the king's high priest has fallen under the influence of anger. He has spoken an untruth. He has told you that crow's fat will cure the wounds on your elephants' backs. But the truth is, Your Majesty, that crows have almost no fat at all."

The warmth of the crow's voice, and the wisdom of his words caused a great devotion to spring up in the king's heart. He ordered that a royal seat be given to the king of the crows, sweet rice in a golden bowl, and fresh water in a golden dish. The Bodhisatta leapt up onto the seat. He nibbled and drank. And then the king addressed him. He said, "Wise one, tell me this—how is it that crows have almost no fat at all?"

The Bodhisatta let forth a cry that filled the entire house. He said, "The reason is simple, and I shall explain." And he spoke this verse:

With a heart forever anxious, and the whole world at our back
Because of that there is no ounce of fat, for my relatives, the crows.

So the Bodhisatta instructed the king, saying, "Your Majesty, a king's actions ought to follow from careful consideration."

The king was pleased. He honored the Bodhisatta by giving him a kingdom.

But what does a crow want with a kingdom? He gave it back. Instead he asked the king to give up his slaughter of crows, and to this the king agreed. He gave orders that a measure of rice be cooked every day, spiced and flavored to suit a crow, and given as a gift to the crows of the city. And to the Bodhisatta, he offered a meal fit for a king.

※ ❦ ※

STORY CIRCLE PRACTICE

REFLECTIVE QUESTIONS

ॐ *What image or scene stays with you from this story?*

ॐ *What emotions are present in this story?*

ॐ *How do they govern the various characters' actions?*

STORYTELLING

ॐ *As a parent, a teacher, an employer or employee, have you ever consciously prepared yourself for a difficult conversation by calling up particular qualities of mind or heart, such as patience, equanimity, or kindness? What happened?*

Tell a story.

The King of the Animals

HAITI

In Haiti more than half of the population can nei-ther read nor write. As a result, wisdom is oral. People express their knowledge and hand it down in proverbs. In the rural parts of the country, when a serious conversation is underway, it is only a matter of time before someone quotes a proverb in support of an idea. There are hundreds of proverbs. One very famous one is:

Piti, piti, wazo fe nich li.
Little by little the bird builds its nest

It is said that once the animals decided they needed a king. A gathering was called. Drummers marched from one village to another to announce the event. The message was carried in every direction. Preparations were made. A large court was made ready for dancing and celebration. Food was cooked, lots of it. The animals came. There was a tremendous crowd. The tree lizard, Zandolite, was the chairman. He addressed the assemblage.

"Brothers and sisters," he said, "we need a king. In the old days we had a king, and in those times everything was in good order. Nowadays, when we have no king, there is much disorder. Every man is for himself, and there is trouble all around us. Let us select our leader."

There was noisy discussion among the animals. Then someone called out, "Let the bull be our king."

The animals talked among themselves, and at last they said, "No, the bull isn't fit to be king. He is strong, but he likes to fight. He puts his head down and threatens anyone who stands in his way."

Someone said, "Let the goat be king."

They discussed the question again, and after a while the crowd said, "No, the goat doesn't have what a king requires. He eats the leaves off the coffee plants. He stands around for hours munching, with his beard bobbing up and down. Who wants a king who is always eating?"

Someone said, "Let the ram be king."

Again they argued. When they were through discussing it, they said, "We can't have such a creature as that for our king. Every time he meets one of his kind, he wants to fight. But if he meets a large person like the bull, he is very timid and docile. No one would be able to respect him."

"Well, then let the donkey be king," someone suggested.

"What!" the people said in disgust. "The donkey? Should we have for a king a person who carries coffee and charcoal on his back all day? What would people think of us? We need a leader of whom we can be proud."

"Make the guinea cock king," someone said.

"With those red legs of his? With that bald head he has?"

The animals laughed loudly. "Would we want people to say, 'The king of the animals has burned his legs and lost his hair?' Oh, no, not the guinea cock."

"What about the turkey?" someone suggested.

"No, no, not the turkey. He looks too stupid."

"Let us consider the rabbit," another said.

"The rabbit? Whenever someone comes along, the rabbit has to jump out of the way. He hides in the grass. And he twitches his nose. He has no dignity."

"Well, then, let the snake be king."

"The snake?" the crowd answered. "The person who lives in a hole in the ground? If you step on him, he wriggles but never makes a sound of protest. He crawls on his belly. No, he can't be king."

"What about the horse?" someone said.

"Horse? How could we have as king a person with a bit in his mouth and a man on his back? No, no, not the horse."

Each animal whose name came up was rejected for this reason or that. At last only the dog was left.

"Let the dog be king," someone called out.

There was applause. The animals said, "Yes, let us make the dog our leader."

They crowded around him. They started the ceremony to make the dog the king of the animals. The drums were drumming. Flags were waving. The food was cooking. As they dressed the dog in his royal clothes, he smelled the meat cooking over the fire

nearby. It made him very hungry. His mouth watered. They wiped his face. Saliva ran out of his mouth. They wiped his face again. Suddenly, because he couldn't control himself any longer, the dog broke loose, seized the meat in his teeth, and ran away.

"Our king is gone!" everyone shouted.

Then they began to say, "No, he isn't our king. He has stolen the meat. He is a thief. How could we have a thief for our king?"

So the great gathering broke up. Everyone went home.

This is the way it was: every creature that was proposed was rejected because he was judged by his weaknesses. Had they been judged by their strong points rather than their weaknesses, the animals would now have a king. As it is, they do not have one.

❧ ❧ ❧

STORY CIRCLE PRACTICE

REFLECTIVE QUESTIONS

§ *According to what criteria were the animals judging each other?*

§ *What role does judgment play in your work or community?*

§ *Is there a difference between judgment and evaluation?*

STORYTELLING

§ *When and how have you received appreciation for your work? How did it feel?*

Tell a story.

All Things Are Connected

ZAÏRE

Among the Nkundo of Zaïre an excellent storyteller is one who not only selects a tale that is appropriate to the needs of his audience, but is also able to improvise, investing what would otherwise be a routine telling with sufficient flavor and appeal so that his tale is certain to be relished and retold; he "reads" his audience skillfully and by use of intonation, pregnant pause, mime, and vocal mimicry brings the tale home to his listeners.[18]

Long ago, a cruel chieftain ruled a remote village in Africa. He was a tyrant who demanded that his orders be obeyed on pain of death. Everyone lived in fear of him but for an elderly grandmother who had lived long and seen much. She was the only person in the village brave enough to tell the chief the truth.

The village was located near a large marsh inhabited by numerous amphibians and insects. The people were sung to sleep each night by the gentle croaking of frogs. *Crribbitt, crribbitt, crribbitt.*

One night the chief awoke from a bad dream, and couldn't get back to sleep. *Crribbitt, crribbitt, crribbitt* was all he heard. Because he was in a foul mood, the frog's song wasn't at all soothing. It was most irritating. *Crribbitt, crribbitt, crribbitt.*

"Quiet!" cried the chief. "I want all the frogs to stop croaking! I demand silence, and I want it now!"

The frogs weren't used to taking orders from humans, and kept on singing. *Crribbitt, crribbitt, crribbitt.*

The frogs kept him awake for the rest of the night, and the chief wanted revenge. He called the people together early the next morning, and said, "The frogs disobeyed

---

18 Barbara K. Walker, General Introduction, Walker, Barbara K. and Mable H. Ross. *"On Another Day . . ." Tales Told Among the Nkundo of Zaïre.* (Hamden, Connecticut; Archon Books, 1979), p. 42.

me. Go to the marsh with your sticks and kill them. If I hear the croak of a single frog tonight, I'll turn my revenge upon you."

All the villagers, except for the old grandmother, grabbed their sticks and ran to the marsh.

"Since you are so old and slow, I'll allow you to stay in the village," said the chief.

"And since you are so foolish in your demands, I'll tell you what is true," said the grandmother. "All things are connected."

"What does that mean?" asked the chief.

"You will see," replied the brave woman. "You will soon see."

A strange silence engulfed the village that night. Without the song of the frogs to lull them to sleep, the villagers were restless. The chief, however, slept soundly, and was convinced that he had made the right decision.

Several days later, another sound was heard in the village. *Zzzz, zzzz, zzzz.*

Mosquitoes came in swarms and bit everyone in their sleep. *Zzzz, zzzz, zzzz.*

The chief awoke in anger, batting a thousand mosquitoes away from his head. "Leave me alone!" he cried. "Get out of my house or I'll have you killed, too!"

The mosquitoes answered by buzzing even louder, and biting him again and again. *ZZZZ, ZZZZ, ZZZz.*

The following morning, the chief told his people to return to the marsh and kill all the mosquitoes. It was an impossible task, however, as there were far too many insects. Without frogs to eat the larvae, the mosquito population rapidly increased. Thousands upon thousands were hatched each day, and now they ruled the marsh and everything nearby. The village swarmed with hungry mosquitoes, and the animals, as well as the people, suffered. The villagers secretly packed up their belongings and moved far away during the night.

Now, the chief had no one to rule over. At last he understood what the old grandmother had meant. All things are connected.

Crribbitt, crribbitt, crribbitt. . . .

Zzzz, zzzz, zzzz.

Gulp.

❈ ❈ ❈

STORY CIRCLE PRACTICE

REFLECTIVE QUESTIONS

❧ *Is it possible to know the consequences of our actions?*

❧ *In what ways do we place convenience ahead of discomfort?*

STORYTELLING

❧ *When have you been "brave enough to tell the truth"? What were the circumstances? How did it feel?*

Tell a story.

FIVE

SHARING WISDOM

Our species thinks in metaphors and learns through stories.

—MARY CATHERINE BATESON

Sharing wisdom by telling stories is nothing new. In traditional cultures it continues to be the primary means of passing along knowledge and values. And yet, among most North Americans of European descent, this ancient practice has been relegated to bedtime or summer campfires. In a story circle, the folktale told or read aloud becomes a catalyst for the sharing of personal experience. Stories call to stories. And the kinds of stories we tell depend on the ones we're hearing. Stories of generosity naturally remind us that we, too, have stories of giving and receiving. As we begin to speak we discover that telling the tale actually brings the story into being. Where before a particular life event may not have appeared significant, when we bring it forward and give it context, it reveals its deeper meaning in our lives. The very act of shaping a narrative from the fluid material of memory can lead to surprising insights. In a story circle at the Art Gallery of Greater Victoria, held in conjunction with an exhibit of art by South Asian artists, I told the Indian folktale "A Drum." I asked participants what gift they had received which they now found themselves passing along. One woman told a remarkable story of her mother's determination to provide for her family during the Depression. In telling the story she recognized how her mother's example of resolve and love had informed her own life.

Another example comes from The Practice of Story, an evening class offered through the local university.[19] I asked participants to consider the question, "Who are the storytellers in your life?" They reflected; they wrote in their journals, and

---

19 The Practice of Story: Building Community in a Storytelling Circle is run through Royal Roads University Continuing Studies in Victoria, BC. See http://cstudies. royalroads.ca/.

then they told a story. As we listened to each other's stories our circle grew larger. Each of the remarkable storytellers whose stories we were hearing (teachers, neighbors, family friends, grandparents) joined us. We felt enriched and blessed by each other's memories. I sent the participants home with an assignment—to ask the same question of someone else.

Erica, a retired schoolteacher, returned to our next class with an account of her visit to a ninety-six year old friend. She told us how Evelyn was losing her spark as her mobility diminished, as well as her eyesight and hearing. When Erica asked her, "Who were the storytellers in your life?" at first she didn't understand. With a little prompting and some examples, however, Evelyn realized what was meant by "storyteller" and she completely lit up as she remembered her father and his cheeky sense of humor, a gift she realized that he had passed on to her. Erica expressed her delight and amazement at the impact this simple question had on her friend. By inviting her to share her story, she had helped her connect with the gifts in her own life. Given the opportunity, each one of us is a story-maker and a storyteller; each one of us has wisdom to share.

When we recognize the value of hearing each other's voices we are on our way to building healthy communities. Reverend Ronald Reese, a Presbyterian minister in Seattle, leads a storytelling circle for homeless men. Once a week they gather in the church hall. Reverend Reese reads or tells one of the parables of Jesus. The men sit in silence for a minute and then he asks them if any element in the story—any phrase or image—spoke to them. One by one, the men respond. They tell their stories, their memories and hearts sparked by what they've just heard. The discovery they are making, through storytelling, is that we humans are not as alone as we think we are. The narrative of loss or betrayal, of failure or disappointment, of reconnection and hope, the story we thought was ours alone is both unique and universal. Our stories tell us so. In fact, our stories call to each other's stories, like a series of echoes through time, stretching back through the centuries, and reaching across culture and geography.

At Bridges for Women, an organization in Victoria that supports women leaving abusive situations, storytelling is a key piece in women discovering who they are and who they want to be. Over a six-month period, a group of women meet daily to learn skills to strengthen resilience, increase safety and support each other in imagining a better future. At the end of the six-month period, former graduates of the program come back to share their stories of transformation with those about to launch themselves into a new phase of life. Diane Gilliland, a counselor with Bridges for Women, says, "I share myths and stories of women's strength, but what's most meaningful to these women, emerging from the trauma of domestic violence and abuse, is to hear stories directly from their sisters, women who have traveled the same road, stories of how dehumanizing it was, and how they managed to stitch together a stronger sense of self and are now making a life for themselves and their children."

Another organization using stories and storytelling to build relationships is the Victoria Immigrant and Refugee Centre Society. With the help of a theatre director, the Society encouraged immigrant and refugee youth to share their stories of cultural dislocation and traumatic memory in the form of a pastiche of scenes, later assembled to make a play. The play has now been performed in several high schools in Victoria, giving non-immigrant youth real insight into the challenges facing their peers from war-torn regions of the world, as well as empowering the youth themselves.

The stories in this final section remind us that sharing wisdom happens when we listen, when we give our attention deeply and when we value the ideas of others. The story circle makes space for this to happen.

Three Fridays

PERSIAN

Author and storyteller Celia Lottridge writes: "When my mother was a small girl, she lived in a mission compound in the north-western part of Persia. This meant that she grew up with Mullah Nasrudin. The Turkish people in the area called him Nasrudin Hodja, but to the Persians he was Mullah and he was part of everyday life. There was a Mullah Nasrudin story for every household and village situation, and I think that the Mullah was more like a neighbor than a piece of folklore."

One of Nasrudin Hodja's duties in the village of Akshahir was to give the sermon at the mosque on Fridays. Many Fridays the Hodja enjoyed preaching. He had so much to say and he enjoyed looking down on the upturned faces of the congregation while he spoke words of wisdom inspired by the Koran and by the Hodja's wide experience of village life.

There were other Fridays, however, when the Hodja had nothing to say. It was on just such a Friday that Nasrudin Hodja made his way across the village square, through the great door of the mosque, through the crowd of people who had gathered to hear him, and up into the pulpit. He looked at the beautiful mosaics on the walls, at the carpets on the floor and at the faces below him. Nothing inspired him. His mind was blank. Yet he had to speak.

The Hodja opened his mouth and said, "O people of Akshahir! Do you know and understand what I am about to say to you?"

"No," said the people. "No, we do not."

"What?" said the Hodja. "How can I speak to such ignorant people!" And he gathered his robes around him and descended from the pulpit, free—for one more week.

But this week, like all others, passed; and once again the Hodja found himself climbing into the pulpit with no idea at all of what he was going to say. He did notice that the mosque was quite crowded. There were many more faces than usual gazing up at him expectantly.

Once again the Hodja opened his mouth and spoke. "O people of Akshahir! Do you know and understand what I am about to say to you?"

"Yes, Hodja, we do," answered the people, who remembered what had happened the week before.

The Hodja beamed down at them. "Wonderful!" he said. "Then there is no need for me to speak to you today." And he gathered his robes around him and descended from the pulpit. Free—for one more week.

It was indeed rare for Nasrudin Hodja to go for three weeks without inspiration, but this time it happened. Another Friday came and the Hodja still had nothing to say. Others, however, had had much to say, and news of the Hodja's strange words had traveled far and wide. Indeed the Hodja had some trouble pushing his way through the throng in the mosque, and looking down from the pulpit he saw many strange faces among the familiar ones from the village.

The Hodja smiled. "O people of Akshahir!" he said. "Do you know and understand what I am about to say to you?"

Now, some people in the congregation thought of the week before and they answered, "No, Hodja, we do not." But others, thinking of the week before that, said, "Yes, Hodja, we do!"

"Wonderful!" said Nasrudin Hodja. "Wonderful! Let those who know tell those who do not know."

And Nasrudin Hodja gathered his robes around him and descended from the pulpit. Free. For one more week.

STORY CIRCLE PRACTICE

ॐ *What or who do you consider a source of wisdom in your life?*

ॐ *Where do you find inspiration?*

ॐ *When have you been surprised by finding wisdom in an unlikely place?*

Tell a story.

What Happens When You Really Listen

A TALE FROM SOUTH INDIA

To understand this delightful folktale, it is helpful to know a little bit about the Rāmāyana, one of the great epics in Indian literature. The story addresses important themes including honor, duty, and the challenge of living a moral life. Many versions exist, even some with happy endings. In a nutshell, Rāma, an avatar of the god Vishnu, is the rightful heir to the kingdom of Ayodhya. He is exiled to the forest for fourteen years because of the machinations of his father's wife Kaikeyi. Rāma's faithful wife Sita and his brother Lakshmana accompany him. They live happily in the forest until the demon king Ravana abducts Sita. Hanuman, son of the Wind God, comes to Rāma's aid and offers to help him bring back his wife. War follows. Ravana is killed and Sita and Rāma are reunited, though at first Rāma refuses to take Sita back because she has lived in the household of another man.

In 1987, a television serial based on the Rāmāyana was broadcast on Indian television. An estimated 80 million people tuned in every Sunday morning. This was more than just watching television however. People prepared for the broadcast by bathing. They set garlands around the television set, and considered the viewing of Rāma (or the actor who portrayed him) as a religious experience.[20]

---

20   Paula Richman, editor, *Many Rāmayanas: The Diversity of a Narrative Tradition in South Asia.* (Berkeley, California: University of California Press, 1991), p. 3.

A villager who had no sense of culture and no interest in it was married to a woman who was very cultured. She tried various ways of cultivating his taste for the higher things of life, but he just wasn't interested.

Once, a great reciter of the *Rāmāyana* came to the village. Every evening he would sing, recite, explain the verses of the epic. The whole village went to see this one-man performance as if it were a rare feast.

The woman who was married to the uncultured dolt tried to interest him in going to the performance. She nagged him and nagged him to go and listen. Her husband grumbled, but decided to humor her. So he went in the evening and sat at the back. It was an all-night performance and he just couldn't stay awake. He slept through the night. Early in the morning, when a canto was over and the reciter sang the closing verses for the day, sweets were distributed according to custom. Someone put a few sweets into the mouth of the sleeping man. He woke up soon after and went home. His wife was delighted that her husband had stayed through the night and eagerly asked him how he had enjoyed the *Rāmāyana*. He said, "It was very sweet." His wife was happy to hear it.

The next day his wife again insisted on his going to listen to the epic. So he went to the enclosure where the reciter was performing, sat against a wall, and before long fell fast asleep. The place was crowded, and a young boy sat on his shoulder and made himself comfortable and listened open-mouthed to the fascinating story. In the morning when the night's portion of the story came to an end, everyone got up and so did the husband. The boy had got off earlier, but the man felt the aches and pains from the weight he had borne all night. When he went home and his wife asked him eagerly how it was, he said, "It got heavier and heavier by morning." The wife said, "That's the way that story is." She was happy that her husband was at last beginning to feel the emotions and the greatness of the epic.

On the third day, he sat at the edge of the crowd and was so sleepy that he lay down on the floor and even snored. Early in the morning, a dog came that way and pissed into his mouth a little before he woke up and went home. When his wife asked him how it was, he moved his mouth this way and that, made a face, and said, "Terrible. It was so salty." His wife knew something was wrong, asked him exactly what had happened and didn't let up till he finally told her how he had been sleeping through the performance every night.

On the fourth day, his wife went with him. She sat down in the very first row and told him sternly that he should keep awake no matter what. So he sat dutifully in the front row and began to listen. Very soon he was caught up in the adventures and the characters of the great epic story. On that day, the reciter was enchanting the audience with the story of Hanuman the monkey and how he had to leap across the ocean to take Rāma's signet ring to Sita, the abducted wife of Rāma. When Hanuman was making his leap, the signet ring slipped from his hand and fell into the ocean. Hanuman didn't know what to do. He had to get the ring back quickly and take it to Sita in the demon's kingdom. While he was wringing his hands, the husband, who was listening with rapt attention in the first row, said, "Hanuman, don't worry. I'll get it for you." Then he jumped up and dived into the ocean, found the ring on the ocean floor, and brought it back and gave it to Hanuman.

Everyone was astonished. They thought this man was something special, blessed by Hanuman and Rāma. Ever since, he has been respected in the village as a wise elder, and he has also behaved like one. That's what happens when you really listen to a story, especially the *Rāmāyana*.

❈ ❦ ❈

STORY CIRCLE PRACTICE

REFLECTIVE QUESTIONS

❧ *What brings you awake?*

❧ *Who helps you to listen?*

Stories are being told all around us. Some are life-affirming, others less so.

❧ *When have you found yourself entering the story? Was that a good thing?*

STORYTELLING

❧ *In your lifetime of listening, have there been occasions when you listened very deeply? Is there one that stands out? How were you changed by that experience?*

Tell a story.

The Old Alchemist

BURMA

A new literary form developed in Burma during the 19th century during the early period of British colonial rule. Thingazar Sayadaw, a monk in Upper Burma, invented the Monk's Tale. Satirical in aim, the Monk's Tale was neither a fable, nor a Jataka tale (a story of the Buddha's former lives.) Instead, it drew the attention of the villagers to the religious controversies raging around them—the attacks on Buddhist beliefs by Christian missionaries and the extremes of laxity and puritanism within the different monastic orders of Burma. The tales, with their vivid images of village life, were composed on the spot by monks in the course of a Dharma talk. By word of mouth they reached villages all over the country and soon took their place alongside the Jataka in the repertoire of the village storytellers.

Once upon a time, there lived an old man with his beautiful daughter. She fell in love with a handsome lad, and the two married with the old man's blessing. The young couple led a happy life, except for one problem: the husband spent his time working on alchemy, dreaming of a way to turn base elements into gold. Soon enough, he ran through his patrimony, and the young wife struggled to buy food each day. At last she asked her husband to find a job, but he protested. "I am on the verge of a breakthrough!" he insisted. "When I succeed, we will be rich beyond our dreams!"

Finally the young wife told her father about the problem. He was surprised to learn that his son-in-law was an alchemist, but he promised to help his daughter and asked to see his son-in-law the next day. The young man went reluctantly, expecting a reprimand. To his surprise, his father-in-law confided in him, "I, too, was an alchemist when I was young!" The father-in-law inquired about the young man's work, and the two spent the afternoon talking. Finally the old man stirred with excitement.

"You have done everything I did!" he exclaimed. "You are surely on the verge of a breakthrough. But you need one more ingredient to change base elements into gold, and I have only recently discovered this secret." The old man paused and sighed. "But I am too old to undertake the task. It requires much work."

"I can do it, dear father!" the young man volunteered. The old man brightened. "Yes, perhaps you can." Then he leaned over and whispered, "The ingredient you need is the silver powder that grows on banana leaves. This powder becomes magic when you plant the bananas yourself, and cast certain spells upon it."

"How much powder do we need?" the young man asked.

"Two pounds," the old man replied.

The son-in-law thought out loud, "That requires hundreds of banana plants!"

"Yes," the old man sighed, "and that is why I cannot complete the work myself."

"Do not fear!" the young man said, "I will!" And so the old man taught his son-in-law the incantations and loaned him money for the project.

The next day, the young man bought some land, and cleared it. He dug the ground himself, just as the old man had instructed him, planted the bananas, and murmured the magic spells over them. Each day he examined his plants, keeping weeds and pests away, and when the plants bore fruit, he collected the silver powder from the leaves. There was scarcely any on each plant, and so the young man bought more land, and cultivated more bananas. After several years, the young man collected two pounds of the magic dust. He rushed to his father-in-law's house.

"I have the magic powder!" the young man exclaimed.

"Wonderful!" the old man rejoiced. "Now I can show you how to turn base elements into gold! But first you must bring your wife here. We need her help."

The young man was puzzled, but obeyed. When she appeared, the old man asked his daughter, "While your husband was collecting the banana powder, what did you do with the fruits?"

"Why I sold them," the daughter said, "and that is how we earned a living."

"Did you save any money?" the father asked.

"Yes," she replied.

"May I see it?" the old man asked. So his daughter hurried home and returned with several bags. The old man opened them, saw they were full of gold, and poured the coins on the floor. Then he took a handful of dirt, and put it next to the gold.

"See," he turned to his son-in-law, "you have changed base elements into gold!"

For a tense moment, the young man was silent. Then he laughed, seeing the wisdom in the old man's trick. And from that day on, the young man and his wife prospered greatly. He tended to the plants while she went to the market, selling the bananas. And they both honored the old man as the wisest of alchemists.

❇ ❇ ❇

STORY CIRCLE PRACTICE

REFLECTIVE QUESTIONS

§ *What are you passionate about?*

§ *Who in your life has deeply understood and shared your passion?*

§ *Who has supported you in your pursuit? And likewise, whose passion do you understand and support?*

STORYTELLING

§ *What have you learned from pursuing your passion that you have applied in other areas of your life?*

Tell a story.

Appendix I

STORY WATER/STORY WISDOM
by Margo McLoughlin
(reprinted from *Parabola Magazine,* Summer, 2011)

A story is like water
that you heat for your bath.

It takes messages between the fire
and your skin. It lets them meet,
and it cleans you!

Very few can sit down
in the middle of the fire itself
like a salamander or Abraham.
We need intermediaries.

These lines come from "Story Water", a poem written by the thirteenth century Sufi poet and mystic Jelalludin Rumi.[21] The poem has become a touchstone for me in the work I am doing with stories—asking them to be intermediaries; putting them to work in the service of communities. I believe it is the distilled wisdom of folktales, told and retold over centuries, that makes them fluid and mirror-like, naturally flowing from one cultural context to another, easily reflecting the issues and concerns of the place where they land.

In 2003 I was completing my Master of Divinity at the Harvard Divinity School when I was hired along with other researchers to gather world folktales of generosity for the John E. Fetzer Institute, a non-profit foundation based in Kalamazoo, Michigan. The initial phase of the project was research-driven—to see how different world cultures teach the very basic and essential quality of generosity, in all its manifestations, from the sharing of resources to forgiveness, collaboration, and wise leadership. After combing through folktale collections from Harvard's many

---

21   Coleman Barks with John Moyne, trans., *"Story Water"* in *The Essential Rumi*. (San Francisco: HarperSanFrancisco, 1995), p. 171.

libraries and corresponding with scholars and storytellers, I put together a database of over two hundred tales, many of which are now available to educators and the general public on the Council of Michigan Foundations' website.[22] Gathering this material was in itself useful, and making it available to educators and the general public affirmed its potential in the field of education.

The second phase of the project led my colleagues and me to exploring the potential of these stories to invite a level of discussion that was both meaningful and productive. What if these stories of generosity could be used in community settings to build relationships and spark dialogue? What healing potential did the stories offer for professions with a high degree of burn-out such as politics, education, medicine, and social justice?

In 2005 the Fetzer Institute's "Generosity of Spirit" project launched a series of pilot retreats to find out how these stories might serve in different settings and with different groups, from congressional staffers to medical faculty at the University of Indiana and from teachers in Michigan to social justice activists in Mississippi.

What we discovered is that the story "goes to work" on at least three levels. First, the shared experience of hearing the story builds relationships in an easy, non-confrontational way. Second, the images in the story open the imagination of the listener and suggest new perspectives, new ways of being. Rather than teaching in a didactic manner, the folktale's lessons reach the heart of the listener indirectly, entering through the imagination, as well as through the body's silent collaboration in the unfolding events of the narrative. Third, the opportunity to reflect on the story together offers the story circle's participants a rich opportunity to learn about each other.

One of our first Generosity of Spirit pilot retreats took place in Indianapolis, in partnership with the University of Indianapolis, where research and innovation in the field of patient-centered care had been underway for several years. In a preliminary visit, Mark Nepo, at that time a senior program officer at Fetzer, had interviewed Dr. Rich Frankel and others about what the current issues were for physicians and medical educators. This would help us determine what stories we might use in the story circle. For two days my colleagues (Wayne Muller and Mark Nepo) and I met in a large circle with participants from the medical community associated with the university.

When we arrived we learned how the medical school had chosen to radically change its admission policy, giving more importance to the admission interview than to academic performance—the aim being to admit applicants whose presence in the interview revealed the ability to show empathy, rather than admitting students who were drawn to the profession largely on the basis of potential future income and status. The theme of generosity of spirit spoke directly to the philosophy and culture

---

22 www.learningtogive.org/materials/folktales.

they wished to embody as professors, staff, and physicians. The stories we used in Indianapolis (where we met in a conference room on the grounds of the zoo) were particularly apt: "A Drum," and "The Origin of Different Water Animals," both folk-tales from India.[23] "A Drum" is about the circular nature of generosity: How, when it is understood and expressed in a certain way, it is much more than a one-to-one inter-action—it creates a flow of energy that circulates through the community, affecting more than one other person and ultimately benefiting the individual who initiated the first gift. But more than this, generosity generates meaning: Lewis Hyde, in his book *The Gift* touches on what I believe is the essential element in gift exchange, or any act of generosity, and that is the creation of meaning. He writes: "Gifts, given or received, stand witness to meaning beyond the known, and gift exchange is therefore a transcendent commerce, the economy of recreation, conversion, or renaissance."[24] Walt Whitman's daily visits to Carver Hospital in Washington, D.C., during the Civil War, where he dispensed gifts to the young soldiers—small gifts of money, peaches, ice cream, clean shirts, and handkerchiefs, as well as the gift of his interest, concern, and care—were remembered by him as the happiest times in his life. In giving his care and affection, and in receiving gratitude and appreciation, he found a depth of meaning he hadn't known before.

If we give without expectation of return, we may be surprised by the blessings that flow back to us. As we have discovered when we share these stories in differ-ent settings, every listener brings a unique perspective to interpreting the story. In Indianapolis, one of our retreat participants was from India and had grown up with the story. A professor of linguistics, she shared with us how the story had been a teaching tale for her in two ways: First it was about recognizing the truth of abun-dance, that there is always more available to us in the world than we realize, and second, that even when we think we have nothing, we may have something to give that is just what someone else needs at that moment.

On the second day of the retreat Rich Frankel told us how the first day of being in the circle had affected his morning: "I started the day with surgery students at 7:00 a.m. asking myself, 'What's trying to happen here?' There was a luminous qual-ity present, because of the openness of this process. The students started to come forward with their own stories. Then, I had an admissions interview. I found myself being open to the story this applicant wanted to tell." Through the experience of hearing these stories of generosity, Dr. Frankel had been reminded that personal narratives are also gifts that we give and receive. Generosity is present on both sides

---

23   See page 62 and 72 in this anthology.

24   "*A Drum*" beautifully reflects the lessons that Lewis Hyde describes in his seminal book, *The Gift: Imagination or the Erotic Life of Property* (New York, Random House, 1983).

of the exchange. And, in the field of healthcare, the way a narrative is received can have a profound impact on an individual's healing.

In Mississippi, at two different weekend retreats, the circle was composed of people from Greenwood and Ittabeena, in the Mississippi Delta. These are folks who care deeply about the place they call home. Some of them grew up in the Delta. Some left and have returned to retire. Others have arrived here from elsewhere. They describe Greenwood as a place that is still racially divided, with the river separating the more prosperous part of the city from Baptist Town, an African-American neighborhood with high unemployment rates. Besides geographical divisions there is also division in the education system. The public schools are under-funded, principally because the white population doesn't attend and see only a small percentage complete their high-school education. Pilloh Academy, the predominantly white institution that was founded in the Sixties during the era of integration, sends most of its graduates on to university.

Under the auspices of the Winter Institute for Racial Reconciliation in Oxford, Miss., these individuals had come to a lakeside resort in Louisville to attend a pilot "Welcome Table" retreat, a chance to see if the story circle model might be of use to them in their work of building community.[25] In the circle was a fire-fighting chief, a retired college professor, a retired physician and member of the National Guard, a high-school student, a pastor, a member of the Chamber of Commerce, and several other members of the community.

Among other stories, I told "The Antelope Birth," one of the Buddhist Jataka (narratives that tell of the Buddha's former lives). The story resonated strongly here because it's about the art of collaboration. Three very different creatures work together to help each other.

"They recognized each other's unique skills," said Bill, a retired college professor and former high school teacher and basketball coach.

"They took a risk," said another participant.

"They didn't procrastinate. They weren't waiting for someone else to come along and tell them what to do."

"They got to know each other by telling stories and then, when a crisis happened, they were ready to work together."

Each of these reflections demonstrates the power of the story as a fluid metaphor, one that "is only waiting for a new context to reveal new meaning."[26] In Buddhist India the narrative is about the embodiment of loving-kindness or friendliness. When he is caught in the hunter's leather snare, the antelope's loyal friends, the turtle and the woodpecker, set to work to free him. The woodpecker

---

25 Other collaborators on this project were the Fetzer Institute and the Kellogg Foundation.

26 Ramanujan, *Folktales from India,* p. xxii.

uses his wings to startle the hunter and slow him down, while the turtle uses his sharp beak to cut and chew the leather snare. The antelope escapes the snare but the turtle, too exhausted by his exertion, cannot move fast enough to elude the hunter when he returns. Finding his snare empty, the hunter is at first disappointed, but then decides that a turtle is just as good as an antelope. He collects the turtle, placing him in his leather pouch, but the antelope, looking back as he runs down the trail, sees that his friend has been captured and returns to rescue him.

In the story the enemy is a hunter, just doing what hunters do. But in Mississippi, the enemy is complacency, a culture of sometimes subtle and often overt racism.

When I told the story at a second Welcome Table retreat for participants from Greenwood, held in Louisville in January 2010, it elicited similar but slightly different responses. As I listened to the participants responding, I became aware that while each had a unique experience in the course of listening to the story, as soon as they began to share their responses, they were also learning about each other and building upon each other's ideas. The story's meaning was extended and deepened by the discussion.

"It speaks to where we are," said one person. "We're such a diverse group."

"They picked up each other's slack," said another.

Alice, a former corrections officer, offered these thoughts: "[The animals] shared the same space. What happened to one affected the other. They came together."

Dash, a young African-American man in his mid-20s, who grew up in Chicago, talked about how the story showed each of the characters learning to try something that wasn't necessarily part of their nature: "The turtle told stories that were long and slow, but he had to work quickly to free the antelope. The antelope, who was used to moving around quickly, had to be patient. The woodpecker had to show bravery. He was on top of his game."

Another listener said, "[It just shows you] what we can accomplish when we combine our strengths."

Leroy, a member of the facilitation team who is from Philadelphia, Mississippi said: "They combined their different skill sets."

To which Ricardo added, "They had a plan."

Sally took this one step further: "But when the story changed they had to change the plan."

Nathan, a retired musician, said, "The story tells that there's always something you can do, if only not to tolerate it." (*It* in this case is the drama of capture in the story and the truth of racism in Greenwood.)

Leroy returned to his comment about skill sets: "How can a turtle rescue an antelope? You never know what skill-set a person is bringing. You never know. That's the beauty of community."

It was powerful to hear the ideas flying back and forth across the circle. On one level we were talking about a simple story of friendship and collaboration. On another level, we were identifying the potential of a community.

Sometimes we do need intermediaries—stories or poems that help us shift our perception, that remind us who we are and what we can become.

Appendix II

Stories from the Story Circles

Stories Call to Stories

At a Spirit of Justice retreat in Mississippi I told "The Blind Man Catches a Bird."[27] In the story from Zimbabwe, a young man takes his blind brother-in-law trapping. They both lay traps for birds. The sighted man camouflages his own trap, but can't be bothered to do the same for his brother-in-law. The next day, when they return, both have caught birds, but the blind man's bird has more beautiful feathers, all the colours of the rainbow, and they arouse envy in the heart of the young man. The feathers would make a fine gift for his new wife. He substitutes his own plain bird for his brother-in-law's, not expecting him to notice. But he does.

The story is about blindness, both literal and figurative. When we take from others whom we assume to be blind to what we are doing, those whom we consider ignorant, we absolve ourselves of guilt, believing that their lack of awareness cancels out our responsibility. Since they don't know what their rights are how have we perpetrated any crime? But we are ourselves are ignorant, because the blind one knows what has happened on much deeper levels than we can guess at. The blind one knows by our tone of voice, by our gestures, by our movements. Deception and greed cannot be disguised, especially not from ourselves. It is the self-deception that is most dangerous. Once we begin to believe our own lies, we are in danger of becoming completely separated from our own potential for goodness and connection.

The story called up a story from one of the participants. Jackie was a high-school student in McComb, Mississippi, in 1961 when another student—a senior—was expelled for participating in civil rights activities. Jackie and others walked out in support of her. They were not allowed to finish their education at their high school.

But the story that came to Jackie's memory was not about her high-school years. It went farther back, to her childhood growing up in McComb. She and her

---

27   See *Peace Tales: World Folktales to Talk About* by Margaret Read MacDonald (Little Rock, AK: August House, 1992).

siblings used to play in a vacant lot between L street and St. Augustine. Her cousin's great-grandfather was a blind man known as Grandpa Butler who lived on St. Augustine. After school, when they were going out to play, the children would go over to Grandpa Butler's house and collect him. They would lead him, with his cane, across the street, and settle him on a bench under the live-oak trees so he could listen to the children playing and act as referee for their game. He knew all the children by their voices. They would sometimes try to trick him with coins, getting him to guess what he was holding. But he always knew. He would settle their squabbles, and then, after they had done playing, he would tell them stories about his own childhood, before the turn of the twentieth century. He had a deep, baritone voice, remembers Jackie, and he never had to raise it to get the children's attention. Instead, he would drop it and the children would gather close to listen.

That's what he taught them—how to listen. Not just to him and his stories, but to the sounds of nature.

"That is something that you can always draw upon, to connect you with a stranger," says Jackie, "Your experience of hearing the wind, or the rain, or the song of a bird. Mr. Butler, Grandpa Butler, taught me that."

Storytelling with Dessert

In the fall of 2011, I gave a four-part evening class called "The Practice of Story: Building Community in a Storytelling Circle." One of the participants wrote about leading a storytelling circle with her family. The Chinese folktale she refers to is "The Lost Horse," and can be found in Moss Roberts, *Chinese Fairy Tales and Fantasies* (New York: Pantheon Books, 1979), p. 82. The story explores how events can be seen as a blessing or a curse.

Kirsten writes:

At the end of a family dinner, over tea and dessert, we did a storytelling circle. I first told the story of "The Lost Horse," and then invited anyone who felt willing to share a story, either about a time when they were in a situation that they at first thought of one way, but later saw it another way, or alternatively they could tell a story about a gift they were given that they then shared or passed on in some way. We went around the circle and each person told a story. It was a great experience. Some of the stories had us laughing, and others had us in tears.

For example, my mother told this great story about how early in their marriage my father had given her the "gift" of a broom for her birthday. At the time she was so upset, because it offended her feminist values. She had to explain to my father that a clean house was a gift that both her and my father were to give to the family, not just her! Her description of the circumstances surrounding this "gift" had me and my sisters and even my father rolling in laughter. She then explained how whenever she uses that same broom she thinks of her important role in the family and how much her and my father have grown together over the years.

My sister told a story about her son. When she first found out about being pregnant with her son at only 17 years old, she was not thrilled to say the least. At the time she had dropped out of high school and was struggling with drug addiction. Since the birth of her son she has found new purpose in life, is now sober and has obtained her GED and is enrolled for Camosun College for next term. She said, her beautiful baby boy gave her the motivation and inspiration to change her path and now she is so proud of all she has accomplished. He turned out to be the best thing that could have happened to her.

This storytelling circle worked wonderfully. Everyone loved it. I think we will do it again.

Kirsten M., Victoria, BC
M.A. Dispute Resolution

Reflections on the Power of Stories

The source of our life stories resides in the inner chambers of our soul waiting to be shared and, held in the hearts of others. Our stories awaken the inner core of our wholeness, often hidden not just from the world but from ourselves. When we reflect deeply the story is found and nestles in our conscious memory. Our story puts us in touch, more than we ever imagined possible, with ourselves and with others around us.

To tell our story is a gift to the self and the listener. Spoken out loud, the story reveals our hidden wholeness and foreshadows inner wisdom and lessons that guide the way for life's journey. When we share and exchange our stories they teach and connect us to each other. Each story generates a related story from the well of our experiences, knowledge and wisdom while inspiring another story from those who listen. Most of all they bring forth an array of emotions, both in the speaker and the listener. An opening and vulnerability emerges, we dare to be in touch, once again, with the passion that propels us toward a question central to an earthly purpose, "How do we relate to each other unconditionally?"

Stories build work teams, develop "beloved" communities and diminish barriers that separate. Storytelling creates relationships that bond because they reveal our common humanity and mold a foundation out of a deeper understanding of self and the other.

Patricia Moore Harbour,
Educator and certified professional coach

We cannot travel everywhere, meet everyone, and experience everything. That is why we have stories. Stories, our own, and those of other cultures and experiences, are central to the Welcome Table process. They allow us a glimpse into each other's experiences and hearts and thus create a space for deeper learning and cooperation based on our common humanity.

Susan Glisson
Executive Director
William Winter Institute for Racial Reconciliation
University of Mississippi

The stories that Margo McLoughlin shared at the Welcome Table retreats became favorites for young people in communities in Mississippi including students at the University of Mississippi, young people in Greenwood, and in Philadelphia, MS as well as with all the students who attended the Summer Youth Institute. Young people enjoyed the opportunity to engage with stories and to think about generosity, sharing and other concepts in new ways. That engagement helped them personally find and claim their own stories, allowing them to change the trajectory of their course in life. I highly recommend the stories in any setting, but especially with young people and in intergenerational settings.

Patrick Weems
Former youth program director
The William Winter Institute for Racial Reconcilation
University of Mississippi

Notes on the Stories

Dreaming

Page 31 "The Secret of Dreaming" From Jim Poulter *The Secret of Dreaming* (Templestowe, Australia: Red Hen Enterprises, 1988). Author Jim Poulter describes his Aboriginal tale as a "…story I have pieced together over a period of years. During this time I have listened to and read dozens of Aboriginal legends and stories, and have sought from Aboriginal people explanation of the ideas represented in the stories." He adds: "As we know human consciousness is marked by the unique capacity to see future possibilities, and work toward their realization. In other words, the ability to dream. Human dreaming is therefore the direct inheritance of that divine creation dreaming, and this of course is the essential theme of *The Secret of Dreaming*."

Page 38 "The Magic Pillow" Retold from *Traditional Chinese Tales*, translated by Chi-chen Wang. (New York: Columbia University Press, 1944). I came upon this story in *Old Tales for a New Day: Early Answers to Life's Eternal Questions* by Sophia Blanche Lyon Fahs and Alice Cobb. (New York: Prometheus Books, 1980.) Sophia Fahs (1876—1977) was an author, educator and religious activist who believed in the value of experiential learning. When I first began searching for stories of generosity, I was also involved in researching the lives of children for an exhibit curated by Eve Mosley. This led me to various archives at Harvard including the Archives at the Andover-Theological Library, where I was greatly assisted by Fran O'Donnell, the curator of Manuscripts and Archives. It was Fran O'Donnell who recommended the book.

Page 41 "The Snake of Dreams" Retold by Hugh Lupton in *Riddle Me This*. (Cambridge, Mass.: Barefoot Books, 2007). Another source is "The Serpent and the Peasant" in *Folktales of All Nations*, edited by F. H. Lee (New York: Tudor Publishing Company, 1930). Introductory notes from *Ethnography and Folklore of the Georgia-Chechnya Border: Images, Customs, Myths and Folk Tales of the Peripheries by* Shorena Kurtsikidze & Vakhtang Chikovani. (Lincom Europa, 2008) p. x.

Page 46 "The Revolt of the Utensils" Translated and retold by Margo McLoughlin from *Die Tacana: Ergebnisse der Frobenius-Expedition nach Bolivien 1952 bis 1954.* Veröffentlich des Frobenius-Institutes an der Johann Wolfgang Goethe-Universität, Frankfurt am Main. Thank you to Harutyun Harutyunyan for his assistance with the translation.

Giving and Receiving

Page 51 "Mokusen's Hand" is from *Zen Flesh, Zen Bones: A Collection of Zen and Pre-Zen Writings*. Compiled by Paul Reps. (Rutland, Vermont: Charles E. Tuttle, 1957).

Page 53 "Tiggak" was collected by Lawrence Milman and published in his book, *A Kayak Full of Ghosts: Eskimo Tales* (Santa Barbara, California; Capra Press, 1987).

Page 55 "Mullah in the Turkish Bath" is from Eric Daenecke, *Tales of Mullah Nasir-ud-Din: Persian Wit, Wisdom and Folly* (New York: Exposition Press, 1960), 29.

Page 57 "A Quick Crop" from *Sheikh Muzaffer Ozak al-Jerrahi. Irshad.* Translated from the Turkish with an Introduction by Muhtar Holland. (Warwick, New York: Amity House, 1988 and Westport, Connecticut; Pir Publications, 1990), p. 464-65. Reprinted in *Essential Sufism*, edited by James Fadiman and Robert Frager. (Edison, New Jersey: Castle Books, 1998), 190 –91.

Page 59 "Loosening the Stopper" is the retelling of a traditional Hasidic tale by Doug Lipman. See, Doug Lipman, 2000. "Loosening the Stopper." hasidicstories.com. Last modified March 10, 2003. http://www.hasidicstories.com/Stories/Levi_Yitzchak_of_Berdichev/stopper.html

Page 62 "A Drum" is from A. K. Ramanujan, *Folktales from India: A Selection of Oral Tales from Twenty-two Languages* (New York: Pantheon Books, 1991), 226-27.

Page 66 "The Chief of the Well" is retold from: *The Piece of Fire and Other Haitian Tales*, by Harold Courlander. (New York: Harcourt, Brace and Jovanovich, Inc., 1964.)

Page 70 "A Story and a Song" Source: *A Flowering Tree, and Other Oral Tales from India*. A. K. Ramanujan. Edited by Stuart Blackburn and Alan Dundes. (Berkeley: University of California Press, 1997). An earlier version was published in "Toward a Counter-System: Women's Tales," by A. K. Ramanujan in *Gender, Genre, and Power in South Asian Expressive Traditions*, edited by Arjun Appadurai et al., University of Pennsylvania Press, 1991. Notes for the introduction come from this same essay by A. K. Ramanujan. The University of Pennsylvania Press owns copyright on this particular English-language translation of the tale, but it appears courtesy of a Delhi-based publishing house, Sahitya Akademi (India's National Academy of Letters), where it was published in 1972 in the Kannada-language book *Uttara Karnatakada Janapada Kathegalu*, edited by Simpi Linganna.

Page 72 "The Origin of Different Water Animals" in *Folktales of India*, edited by Brenda E. F. Beck, Peter J. Claus, Praphulladatta Goswami and Jawaharlal Handoo. (Chicago: University of Chicago Press, 1987). Introductory notes from *Naked Nagas* by Fürer-Haimendorf. (Calcutta: Tahcker Spink Co., 1939, revised edition 1962).

Working Together

Page 77 "The Wise Quail" in *The Hungry Tigress: Buddhist Myths, Legends, and Jataka*

Tales. Told and with commentaries by Rafe Martin. (Cambridge, Massachusetts: Yellow Moon Press, 1999).

Page 81 "The Antelope, the Woodpecker and the Turtle" Translated from the Pali and adapted by Margo McLoughlin. Pali source: "Kurunga-miga Jataka," in *The Jataka, Together with Its Commentary, Being the Tales of the Anterior Births of Gotama Buddha, for the first time edited in the original Pali by V. Fausböll* (London: Kegan Paul Trench Trubner & Co., Ltd, 1891).

Page 85 "The Friendship Orchard" is from *Eleven Nature Tales: A Multicultural Journey* by Pleasant DeSpain. (Little Rock, Arkansas: August House Publishers, 1996).

Becoming a Leader

Page 91 "The Clever Sheik of the Butana" in *The Clever Sheikh of the Butana and Other Stories: Sudanese Folktales*, retold by Ali Lutfi Abdallah (New York: Interlink Books, 1999), 21-22. W. Stephen Howard, Professor of African Studies at Ohio University, introduces this collection by painting a vivid picture of Sudanese village life. Storytelling is the province of the older women in the village, and tales were often told as children gathered around to eat sorghum or millet porridge from one large pot. As the children listen with wide eyes, the storyteller draws out the syllables to emphasize distance, danger, or size— *kabiiir* for 'big', and *baiiiiid* for 'far'. Each telling of the story will be different, with audience members participating, and the storyteller adapting the story for a particular occasion.

Page 94 "The Wisdom of the Crows" Translated from the Pali Jataka and adapted by Margo McLoughlin. Pali source: "Kaka-Jataka," in *The Jataka, Together with Its Commentary, Being the Tales of the Anterior Births of Gotama Buddha, for the first time edited in the original Pali by V. Fausböll* (London: Kegan Paul Trench Trubner & Co., Ltd, 1891).

Page 98 "The King of the Animals" retold from *The Piece of Fire and Other Haitian Tales* by Harold Courlander (New York: Harcourt, Brace and Jovanovich, Inc., 1964).

Page 101 "All Things Are Connected" in *Eleven Nature Tales: A Multicultural Journey* by Pleasant DeSpain. (Little Rock, Arkansas, 1996), 13-16. Another version can be found in *The Crest and the Hide and other African Stories of Heroes, Chiefs, Bards, Hunters, Sorcerers and Common People* by Harold Courlander (New York: Coward, McCann & Geoghegan, Inc., 1982), p. 103-104.

Sharing Wisdom

Page 114 "The Old Alchemist" in *In the Ever After: Fairy Tales and the Second Half of Life*, by Allan B. Chinen. (Wilmette, Illinois: Chiron Publications, 1992), pp. 31-33. Another version can be found in the prologue to "The Cucumber Alchemist," in *Burmese Monk's Tales*, collected, translated, and introduced by Maung Htn Aung. (New York: Columbia University Press, 1966), p. 41.

Page 108 "Three Fridays is retold by Celia Lottridge in *Tales from an Unknown City: Stories from One Thousand and One Friday Nights of Storytelling*, collected by Dan Yashinsky (Montreal and Kingston: McGill-Queen's University Press, 1990), 15-17.

Page 111 "What Happens When You Really Listen" in *Folktales from India: A Selection of Oral Tales from Twenty-two Languages*, Edited, with an introduction by A. K. Ramanujan. (New York: The Pantheon Fairy Tale and Folklore Library, 1991), p. 55.

Permissions Acknowledgments

Every effort has been made to obtain permission for reprinting the material in this collection. Grateful acknowledgment is made to the following for permission to reprint and adapt from previously published material.

"The Secret of Dreaming" from *The Secret of Dreaming* by Jim Poulter. Copyright © by Jim Pouter, 1988. Reprinted by permission of Jim Poulter.

"The Magic Pillow" adapted from *Traditional Chinese Tales*. Translated by Chi-Chen Wang. Copyright 1976 by Columbia University Press. Reprinted by permission of Columbia University Press.

"The Snake of Dreams" from *Riddle Me This: Riddles and Stories to Sharpen Your Wits* by Hugh Lupton. Copyright by Barefoot Books, 2003. Reprinted by permission of Barefoot Books.

"Mokusen's Hand" from *Zen Flesh, Zen Bones: A Collection of Zen and Pre-Zen Writings*. Compiled by Paul Reps. Copyright by Charles E. Tuttle, 1957. Reprinted by permission of Charles E. Tuttle.

"Tiggak" from *A Kayak Full of Ghosts: Eskimo Tales* by Lawrence Milman. Copyright by Lawrence Millman, 1987. Reprinted by permission of Lawrence Milman.

"A Quick Crop" from *Sheikh Muzaffer Ozak al-Jerrahi. Irshad*. Translated from the Turkish with an Introduction by Muhtar Holland. Copyright Pir Publications, 1990. Reprinted by permission of Pir Press.

"Loosening the Stopper" from Loosening the Stopper (hasisdicstories.com) by Doug Lipman. Reprinted by permission of Doug Lipman.

"What Happens When You Really Listen", "A Drum" copyright © 1991 by A.K. Ramanujan, from *Folktales from India* by A.K. Ramanujan, copyright © 1991 by A.K. Ramanujan. Used by permission of Pantheon Books, a division of Random House, Inc. Any third party use of this material, outside of this publication, is prohibited. Interested parties must apply directly to Random House, Inc. for permission.

Bibliography

Baldwin, Christina. *Storycatcher: Making Sense of Our Lives through the Power and Practice of Story.* (Novato, California: New World Library, 2005).

_____. *Calling the Circle: The First and Future Culture.* (New York: Bantam Books, 1998.)

Block, Peter. *Community: The Structure of Belonging.* (San Francisco: Berret-Koehler Publishers, Inc., 2008).

Cox, Allison M. and David H. Albert. Foreword by Nancy Mellon. *The Healing Heart— Families: Storytelling to Encourage Caring and Healthy Families.* (Gabriola Island, BC: New Society Publishers, 2003).

_____. Foreword by Margaret Read MacDonald. *The Healing Heart—Communities: Storytelling to Build Strong and Healthy Communities.* (Gabriola Island, BC: New Society Publishers, 2003).

Hyde, Lewis. *The Gift: Creativity and the Artist in the Modern World.* (New York: Vintage Books, 2007).

Solinger, Rickie, Madeline Fox, and Kayhan Irani, eds. *Telling Stories to Change the World: Global Voices on the Power of Narrative to Build Community and Make Social Justice Claims.* (New York and London: Routledge, 2008).

Other Resources

For world tales of generosity, visit the Council of Michigan Foundations' website www.learningtogive.org/materials/folktales. You will find the folktales organized by character trait, geography, and religious tradition, as well as by title.

To learn about workshops, or to sign up for a newsletter, please visit www.margostoryteller.net.